This book is one of few that could ri   — ...ionai y — iii more than one sense of the word. All healing is ultimately dependent on our connection with the primordial energetic nature of the cosmos. Disease occurs when that connection becomes obscured and disease crystallizes in the mind-body. Though slowly changing, the modern paradigm still does not recognize the powerful influence of the mind on physical disease. In *Reversing Cancer Through Mental Imagery*, Simcha H. Benyosef lays a foundation for the practical application of mind-body connection.

In performing many of these simple exercises myself for less than a month, I was fascinated by the transformation, which started to occur. I truly began to experience a sense of release from the entrapment of mental, emotional and karmic patterns which were subconsciously encumbering me.
—Scott Gerson, M.D., M. Phil (Ayurveda), Ph. D. (Ayurveda)
Medical Director, The Gerson Institute of Ayurvedic Medicine

⌘

"God said, 'I have given you life and death...choose life' (Deut. 30:19). But how, when you are confronted with the most fearful of diagnosis? This book tells you how, step by step. Faithfully using the revolutionary tools taught by the revered Kabbalist Colette Aboulker-Muscat, Benyosef leads the reader gently and persuasively away from fear and illness towards inner aliveness. The simple, clear imagery taps into the font of healing inside each one of us and awakens latent forces of joy and self-affirmation."
—Catherine Shainberg, author of *Kabbalah and the Power of Dreaming* and *DreamBirth: Transforming the Journey of Childbirth Through Imagery*

⌘

For over four decades, I have sought out and intensively studied the healing methods that get the best results with serious illnesses. I have found IMAGERY exercises to be highly effective with my clients challenged by cancer. The Imagery exercises in this book are a comprehensive program that helps you to be freer, to be uniquely yourself, and to live a more fulfilled life. In my experience, this is the best way to maximize the strength of your immune system. Don't just read this book ... USE IT!
—Robert Jokel, P.T., *Immune To Cancer: Bringing the Full Strength of Your Immune System to the Aid of Your Medical Program* (DVD)

⌘

Cancer can be the final product of a multitude of "causes." Reversing cancer can be a formidable process requiring approaches from as many levels as possible in order to maximize the chances of success.

Throughout the day, we constantly create imagery in our minds that either impair or enhance the immune system (among other things) and its ability to identify and eliminate cancer cells.

In this new book, Benyosef provides a wide variety of exercises to help us more consciously focus our imagery toward healthy immune responses.
—Mel Litman, M.D.
Center for Orthomolecular Medicine, Tel Aviv, Israel

⌘

An extraordinarily important work. Not only does *Reversing Cancer* give a clear and concise method for the use of imagery exercises in cancer, but it offers a rare glimpse into the life and inner workings of a genuine spiritual healer Colette Aboulker-Muscat, Benyosef's teacher. These deceptively simple exercises resonate on many levels. They turn this most dreaded disease into a springboard to a personal connection with the Divine, and the powerful and miraculous healing that is available to all.
—Risa Levenson Gold, M.D.
President, Greater Long Island Psychiatric Society

Reversing Cancer
Through Mental Imagery

Reversing Cancer
Through Mental Imagery

Simcha H. Benyosef

ACMI Press: New York

ACMI Press
351 East 84th Street, Suite 10 D, New York, NY 10028
Tel: (212) 369-4080
www.acmipress.org

This book does not offer medical information or advice and is not intended as a substitute for consultation with physicians. The reader should consult a physician in matters relating to his or her health, particularly in regard to any symptoms that may require diagnosis or medical attention, before making use of the contents of this book. This book is sold without representations or warranties of any kind.

Publisher's Cataloging-in-Publication
  Benyosef, Simcha H.
        Reversing cancer through mental imagery / Simcha H.
    Benyosef. -- 1st ed.
        p. cm.
        Includes bibliographical references and index.
        ISBN-13: 978-1-883148-09-6
        ISBN-10: 1-883148-09-X

        1. Cancer--Psychological aspects. 2. Mental healing.
    3. Imagery (Psychology)--Therapeutic use. 4. Mind and
    body therapies.   I. Title.

    RC271.M4B46 2009   616.99'40651
                        QBI09-600073

Library of Congress Control Number: 2009943990

To Colette,

>*For her gift in bringing forth*
>*the heavenly spark hidden in all of us.*
>*May the Holy One keep her soul*
>*in the Light of Life.*

To You, My Readers,

>*I have tried to transmit in these pages the legacy that Colette left behind: Imagery as a tool of connection between body and spirit as well as a vehicle for healing. May each of you internalize her teachings and learn how to access them for yourself as well as to promote health and well-being in the world.*
>
>>*— Simcha H. Benyosef*

AND

To All Who Suffer,

>*Whatever your difficulties may be, this book shows different ways out of them, and how not to fall again in the same sort of trouble. May you find in this work what is valuable for yourself.*
>
>>*— Colette Aboulker-Muscat*

Author's Acknowledgments

To Colette, for trusting me with the precious document of her life and work.

To my patients, my teachers.

To Dr. Gerald Epstein, for his discerning advice, editing, explications, and support throughout all stages of this book. His insight into the relationship between imagination and healing greatly enhanced this work.

To Rachel Epstein, for her indispensable reorganization, editing, and oversight of this work.

My admiration to Gerald and Rachel Epstein for their faithful expression of gratitude to Colette throughout the years after her demise. The Sages teach that one who denies his fellow's goodness will eventually deny receiving from his Maker's goodness. Rabbi Shalom Arush indicates that the opposite is also true: The way to become aware of the Creator's lovingkindness is to recognize the good received from one's fellow man.

To Rabbi Yishai Hochman, for helping me clarify the goal and structure of this book. His guidance has been an invaluable testimony to deliver the book's message. His discussions with both Colette and me enriched this work.

To Shoshana Helfenbaum, for the dedication with which she gave herself to edit this work, bringing her pursuit of truth and self-healing to enhance the lives of others.

To Raquel Eyal, Tirza Moussaieff, Carol Rose, Catherine Shainberg, and Françoise Tibika, for sharing experiences and going over different parts of the manuscript.

To Rebbetzin Tziporah Heller and Professor Moshe Dickman, for their valuable suggestions regarding the section *For Women Only*.

To Nechama Tehilla, for her expert editing of the final draft of the book.

To Harris Dienstfrey, for his fine editing of the book.

To Virginia Gregory, for her tireless proofreading various drafts of the book.

To the Healer of all life, my gratitude for guiding me toward the completion of this difficult undertaking, and also my prayer: Let these pages be a vessel to extend His love and healing to all who suffer.

Table of Contents

Author's Acknowledgments ix

Foreword by Gerald Epstein, M.D. xiii

Part I: Developing Your Inner Vision

Chapter I — What This Book Offers.. 3

    The World of Images.. 6

    Colette's Teachings 8

    Reversing: The Cornerstone of Healing 13

    How to Use This Book 20

Chapter II — Instructions for Imaging 23

    Doing Imagery.. 25

    Imagery as Poetry.. 29

    Record Your Significant Images 30

    Warm-Up Exercises 30

Part II: Healing the Mindbody

Chapter III — The Core Program: The 12 Phases of Healing 35

    Phase 1 to 12 Overview 36

    Selecting the Monthly Exercise 37

    Tips for Getting Started... 42

    Phase One: Re-rooting Ourselves to Life............................... 44

Phase Two: Messages from Above 49

Phase Three: Blunting the Weapons of Your Body Parts 59

Phase Four: Disease as a Cleansing Light 66

Phase Five: Cleansing Anxiety 72

Phase Six: Cleansing Guilt 84

Phase Seven: Removing Resentment 94

Phase Eight: Detaching from Disease 98

Phase Nine: The Winds of Change.......................... 108

Phase Ten: Living as Vibration 113

Phase Eleven: Descending into the Self.................. 117

Phase Twelve: The Power to Ascend....................... 126

Chapter IV — Stepping Out of Fear and Worry 133

Chapter V — Exercises to Reduce Specific Tumors 137

Chapter VI — The Flame of Hope 152

Part III: Celebrating Life — A Tribute to Colette

Chapter VII — Colette: A Life of Giving 165

Epilogue: Ascent of a Soul............................. 178

Postscript by Catherine Shainberg...................... 181

Appendix

Appendix A: Reconnecting to Our Higher Self 182

Appendix B: Reversing Distressing Emotions and Trauma 189

Appendix C: Nighttime Reversing........................ 194

Appendix D: For Clinicians 202

Endnotes... 227

Index 233

About the Author 239

Foreword

By Gerald Epstein, M.D.

This book provides genuine hope to all who have been touched by cancer — sufferers as well as family, friends, and health caregivers. It presents the most profound intervention that currently exists for the treatment of cancer. In the succeeding pages, you will read about a remarkable healing program with an incredible array of transformative mental imagery exercises unlike any you have ever found for treating this disease.

There are no contraindications, unwanted side effects, or financial costs. All it requires is a commitment of a few minutes each day and an intention to heal.

Reversing Cancer Through Mental Imagery draws on Simcha H. Benyosef's work with cancer patients for more than 20 years under the tutelage of the great healer and teacher, Colette Aboulker-Muscat. Simcha, a longtime student of Colette, has faithfully captured the essence of Colette's healing exercises for cancer patients.

For Colette, cancer represented a crisis point in one's life, a challenge to live or die. At this crossroad, a new path may be taken to take charge of one's life in an entirely new way. In these pages, Simcha provides the map for this journey — a progressive series of imagery exercises practiced over twelve months — to choose life and reverse our pain and difficulties into a renewed way of being.

Colette had one mission — to save lives. For some, she literally brought them back from the brink of death, physically and emotionally. Other souls she shepherded toward the reunion with the One.

Colette began her lifelong healing work at the age of six. A gifted child, she was born with signs that foretold her future destiny to care for the ill and to teach her unique methods to all who crossed her threshold.

During the course of her life many unusual situations presented themselves: aiding and healing wounded soldiers during World War I at the age of eight or nine; exorcising "demons" from thousands of people who believed themselves possessed; curing a former French army hero of his compulsion to murder; and facilitating the healing of hundreds of cancer patients.

This book, a legacy of and a testimony to Colette's genius, seeks to enlist each sufferer's mind, a most powerful healing tool, to enhance the innate capacity to heal through the sense of imagination.

I first met Colette in the summer of 1974 while on sabbatical in Jerusalem. A young Frenchman I met there told me of his remarkable cure from a lifelong depression while working with an Algerian Frenchwoman named Colette who practiced a novel therapy called Waking Dream. Years of psychoanalysis had failed to provide a cure, but a few brief meetings with her transformed him.

I was introduced to Colette a few weeks later. The meeting

with her changed the course of my life. Within five minutes of our conversation I had a life-altering epiphany — a glimpse of another reality. I immediately abandoned my years of training and my worldview (and livelihood) as a psychoanalyst and psychiatrist to pursue this vision and devote myself to the therapeutic use of mental imagery.

As you will discover, in mental imagery we turn inward to connect to an invisible reality that cannot be apprehended by our five senses here in the everyday, objective, material world. Rather, it is a subjective experience where discoveries and revelations are made through this inward turning.

Many people encounter a reality difficult to put into words, often defined as ineffable or indescribable. This ineffability has been denoted by many different terms around the world. Having had a taste of this reality, I call it God; Colette called it the One.

For those of you who do not readily experience this subjective truth, the imagery process often opens you to a different value system that includes an understanding of the veracity of an invisible reality, a power higher than ourselves. The beauty of mental imagery is that it works even if you are skeptical of either its benefits or an invisible realm. As a close relative of Colette's confided in me one day, "I don't believe a thing she says, but everything she does works."

So, what makes this work so unique and so different from other imagery books? Colette understood the power of the mind and how healing takes place. She described the mind as the channel of communication between invisible and visible reality. In more common terms, she comprehended the implications of a mindbody unity far before the New Age movement coined the term.

She created over 15,000 short imagery exercises. She used imagery to heal emotional and physical difficulties — as well as for personal growth and spiritual realization.

Simcha has created a masterful program where you start with your feet squarely planted in the here and now. Each month you choose one or two imagery exercises that clean out the physical, mental, and emotional dross that is burdening you. The dazzling and novel array of visualizations provides a light shock stimulating the healing response. Each month's imagery exercises lend power to you to ascend along your own ladder of freedom to separate yourself farther and farther from illness. Colette stressed that only by separating ourselves from illness could we heal body and soul.

Colette was named *The Most Beloved of Jerusalem*, an award given to her in recognition of the great works she rendered to that most holy city. By extension, this book, under Simcha's hand, bears witness to the love Colette sought to share with everyone.

In November 2003, Colette departed this world shortly before her 95th birthday. Although she is not here to witness the publication of this book, she guided Simcha's hand through its creation. Simcha has continued Colette's legacy and mission of choosing life and saving the lives of countless sufferers and seekers on this earth. God bless!

New York City, 2016

Part I

Developing Your Inner Vision

Chapter I

What This Book Offers

All illness is an opportunity to revive and renew ourselves physically, mentally, and spiritually. Often, our first response to the shock of a cancer diagnosis is a frantic search for outside treatments and answers. In addition to standard medical treatments, many of us invest our energies in changing physical habits. We begin exercising, altering our diets and lifestyles. In contrast, this book has another starting point in mind.

Reversing Cancer through Mental Imagery is built upon the work of the world-renowned teacher of mental imagery Mme. Colette Aboulker-Muscat. Her teachings have been made famous through Gerald Epstein's best-selling book — *Healing Visualizations: Creating Health through Imagery,* Catherine Shainberg's book — *Kabbalah and the Power of Dreaming*, and Colette's collected imagery in *The Encyclopedia of Mental Imagery*.[123]

This book offers a unique approach to cancer healing and disease prevention based on visualization techniques. It focuses on changing or reversing our mental habits and mindsets, changes that in turn are reflected in our physical healing. An important aspect of this approach is that it can complement and enhance any other system of healing you may be using.

Reversing Cancer through Mental Imagery addresses the whole person — mind, body, and spirit — through the use of imagery in a 12-phase progressive program. Over the last decade, modern medicine has begun to expand its horizons past the mechanistic view of illness and cure to recognize not only the powerful role the mind plays in healing outcomes but also the influence of spiritual attitudes and values to catalyze healing. My own therapeutic work has corroborated this finding by teaching people to reconnect to deeper — and higher — levels of consciousness through the simple practice of mental imagery. In using imagery one can repair any disturbing images in the mind's eye, much like an artist corrects a painting. I have found that this exploration of oneself can have profound healing effects on all who engage in it.

For those of you using this manual to heal from cancer, the visualization exercises aim to shrink the tumor physically until it disintegrates. Concurrently, the exercises help to fight the cancer emotionally, healing harmful emotions and enabling you to repair your self-image. In my work, I have found that reversing harmful emotions is a fundamental part of overcoming any life-threatening illness. These exercises also aim to help you let go of the fear of a recurrence or metastasis. When you engage in this work for a few minutes a day, you may find that your inner awareness increases, your consciousness expands, your intuition blossoms, and you feel more at peace with yourself. Once the process of healing is under-way, the self naturally radiates joy and inner strength — essential weapons in the battle against disease.

In recent years, there has been a gradual inclusion of guided imagery and other alternative therapies at medical cancer treatment centers. Most limit the use of visualizations to reducing stress, strengthening the immune system, and coping with surgery and chemotherapy. What sets this book apart is not only the scope and sophistication of the imagery, but the book's focal point. While it addresses the physical facts of cancer, the book takes a much more profound approach to healing, lifting our attention off the physical and looking to the broader fabric of our lives — the areas where we have had patterns of repeated difficulties, most often manifesting in the emotional realm. In this way, the book may be used as a therapeutic aid to address *any* illness, whether physical, spiritual, emotional, or psychological, for the essential components of healing from any disorder always remain the same. Moreover, the program can be applied preventively as well.

Cancer involves intense, unrelenting stress. The imagery exercises in this book are geared to help you find a quiet space within from which you have access to your own warm and loving connection to a Higher Power who is the Source of your life and the Source of all life. Through visual imagery, you find a connection that you learn to elicit and retain, like a rope that you will be able to keep pulling even through times of stress. Among the challenging aspects of serious illness are the confusion, loneliness, and sense of meaninglessness it causes, leading the sufferer to try to find meaning in past actions ("It came because I was not loving enough ... I was judgmental..." etc.). The visualizations in this book aid you to understand that your present suffering is a message of help stemming from the Source of love and healing. This help is directed to you personally so you can identify its provenance and discover the ever-present ties that enable you to ascend to your very own space of connection. As you deepen your imagery practice, you can acquire the gift of remaining there while continuing your involvement in daily life. These ties form a ladder that keeps you connected to your Source. Through the practices in this book, you learn to accept the illness and appreciate its messages. As you proceed, the imagery helps you to detach the illness from suffering, gradually assisting you to distance yourself from the illness until it no longer serves a purpose.

We are all beset by the stress and trauma of modern life, from the non-stop pace of technology, to natural calamities, and the threat of terrorism. In these pages, you receive a guided tour to an inner space of harmony and well-being that is beyond the reach of disease. Here, you become a beacon of light for others as well.

The World of Images

My first encounter with the world of images occurred while I lived in New York City. Johanna, one of my friends, was diagnosed with a rare form of leukemia. My despair and inability to help her gave birth to the idea that when the body seems to fail, the mind could come to the rescue by imagining healing. Totally ignorant of the vast body of literature existing about cancer healing and visual imagery, I told my friend what to imagine before and during chemotherapy and at specific times during the day. The images did not heal the body, but they infused her with joy and faith during her last months of life. I eventually learned the art of imagery from Colette Aboulker-Muscat, who helped thousands of people with her techniques of visual imagery and dream therapy. I met Colette in 1989, shortly after moving to Israel from the U.S., where I had left a successful academic career to study the inner dimension of the Torah. I was fascinated by Colette's exceptional success healing malignant diseases through imagery and soon became one of her regular visitors.

A few years later, an acquaintance, Hannah, a deeply religious woman, had a recurrence of cancer. I suggested she go to Colette, but Colette had stopped seeing patients by then; instead she referred Hannah to another student in Jerusalem. Hannah worked with this therapist for a few weeks and felt that the imagery was helping her. Nonetheless, she confided in me that she was averse to working with a therapist who told her to see herself opening the window and thanking the sun for a beautiful day. "The work of mental imagery is closely connected to my relationship to God," Hannah told me. "You work with me instead." I objected that even if I were to start studying Colette's healing technique immediately, Hannah did not have the time to wait. The young woman would not take no for an answer and I stopped hesitating as a result. In view of the situation, Colette agreed to give me a private tutorial on healing imagery that enabled me to acquire this art more quickly than usual. Since then, I have been working with cancer patients for nearly two decades while continuing my studies on the inner meaning of consciousness. I have come to realize that the means to both spiritual fulfillment and health is a shift to a higher plane of awareness; this awareness is inherent in the practice of imagery.

With Colette's encouragement, I decided to write this guide that took me ten years to complete. The exercises are Colette's.

The background material and arrangement of the exercises in this 12-phase progressive program are derived from my understanding of Colette's work as well as my own explorations and observations.[4]

Colette was a genius in this field and drew her inspiration from many sources. Sources are footnoted in the exercises. *Reversing Cancer through Mental Imagery* is one of two books I developed based on Colette's imagery and teachings. Together they form a complete representation of the work she taught me. The other book, *Empowered to Heal: Therapeutic Visualizations Drawn for the Lunar Months* presents visualizations and studies based on the Jewish calendar.[5]

Colette's wisdom permeates this book. I have included a brief biography of this unusual woman and her adventures both in the inner realms of the imagination and the outer realms working to heal the suffering of the world. I hope her life story will imprint in you that you too have the inner power and resources to heal, and inspire you to take an active role in bringing this about.

Colette's Teachings

Colette taught that each one of us has an inner voice that can potentially guide us to healing and transformation by reconnecting us with our personal Source of Life. The function of imagery is to help us hear this voice amplifying the message of the Source of Life. This inner work helps you come back to your true Self and in doing so you become a renewed being, aware of new levels of life and healing. As we will explore in the pages to come, these progressive exercises of ascent, removing illness and scars of the past, elevate your physical body while restoring you to the perfect being you were when you came into the world.

When I came upon the imagery process with Colette, she pointed out that imagery is the Language of the Divine. At the same time, Colette was very careful to modify imagery in order to make it available to every individual, regardless of his/her belief and orientation. While she readily included God's healing hand in her imagery to those who could relate to it, she also explained:

Healing is for all those who need it; and as healing facilitators; it is up to us to offer our means of healing — the imagery — in a way that is acceptable to the sufferer. Hence, whether you refer to God as the One, the Absolute, the Source of Life and healing, or the Force behind nature, it really does not matter, for the patient's higher self, that knows, hears, and understands, will facilitate healing in the best possible way for each individual.

I have learned this lesson from Colette. In this book, when I refer to the Source of Life as "God," you may hear in it whatever way your higher self guides you to. Whatever your philosophical, spiritual, or religious orientation is, there are a multitude of imagery exercises to suit every palate. Just bear in mind that our aims are united: To help you shed cancer (or chronic illness) forever and reconnect to your Source of Life.

There are many co-factors leading to the onset of cancer. In my clinical experience, I have often, but not always, found emotional stress or sudden shock to be contributors to the onset of illness. However, I have had patients honestly bewildered by statements that link cancer to emotional stress. As Lydia put it, "What did I do to bring this on myself?" Lydia was happily married to a man whose devotion to her was very moving, and try as she might, she was unable to find a trauma, shock, or emotional disturbance in her past that could be linked to the disease. Without identifying any emotional sources, Lydia successfully utilized the program in this book to let go of the "whys" tying her to past experience. She then made full use of the additional level of consciousness now available to her and focused it on healing.

Sometimes patients come to me feeling guilty that they somehow have "created" the cancer. These feelings can be as destructive as the disease itself, sapping us of our will to heal. In redirecting the patients away from these unproductive feelings, I encourage them to see the illness not as self-imposed punishment, but rather a challenge sent to those equipped with an inner strength on which they may draw to transform the illness into new levels of growth and healing. Rather than feeling guilty and/or victimized by the illness, they gradually come to see it as a foundation upon which they were able to ascend to a higher purpose in their lives. Elizabeth Kübler-Ross writes of this shift:[6]

When people are buffeted by seemingly endless windstorms and their lives look like calamities, they may wonder why they have been given so many tests, and why God appears to be so merciless. Going through hardship is like being a rock in a tumbler. You're tossed to and fro and get bruised, but you come out more polished and valuable than ever. You are now prepared for even bigger lessons, bigger challenges, and a bigger life. All the nightmares are turned into blessings that become part of living. If we had shielded the Grand Canyon from the windstorms that created it, we would not see the beauty of its carvings. That may be why so many patients have told us that if they could magically go back to the point right before they got their cancer or other life-threatening disease and erase what was to come, they would not.

In my work with both patients and families, I focus on how to harness the challenge of illness to become aware of their special mission in this world and realign their lives accordingly. When cancer is viewed under such a prism, the energy that would otherwise be wasted on self-oriented guilt is free to be devoted to the healing process.

In this paradigm, healing is a force for growth and evolution to a higher state of consciousness in which the challenge of illness no longer applies to the true Self. Through the practice of mental imagery, we can attain this higher state of consciousness beyond the reach of disease, in which we may ascend and reconnect to the Source of Life. As Deepak Chopra writes:

Research on spontaneous cures of cancer . . . has shown that just before the cure appears, almost every patient experiences a dramatic shift in awareness. He knows that he will be healed, and he feels that the force responsible is inside himself but not limited to him — it extends beyond his personal boundaries, throughout all of nature. Suddenly he feels, "I am not limited to my body. All that exists around me is part of myself." At that moment, such patients apparently jump to a new level of consciousness that prohibits the existence of cancer. Then the cancer cells either disappear . . . or at the very least stabilize, without damaging the body any further.[7]

For many, this shift in awareness is a key to healing. It does not have to come in a flash, but can be cultivated deliberately through the use of imagery. Through your own journey of healing, you may discover that suffering has been a precious gift that catalyzes you to change your relationship to the world, to find your unique mission, and to open up to a reality whose ethereal nature you are invited to perceive. Many of my clients have reported that through the work of imaging they have reconnected to the immensity of Divine love and healing and discovered a renewed being within themselves.

Imagery is the natural and true expression of the inner life, a non-verbal pictorial language that conveys information from the invisible reality of our Source of Life to our tangible existence. Disease often manifests itself as a reflection of unprocessed emotions sapping our energy and making our immune system inefficient. Imaging becomes an excellent tool to break out of the mental prison of these emotions and light the way to health. On a mental level, it teaches us to respond emotionally and intellectually in a new way when faced with distressing stimuli. On a physical level, it teaches cancer cells to reverse their self-destructive patterns and the immune system to function efficiently. We can also use imagery to see in our mind's eye what contributed to the cancer and realign our lives to correct our errors. In this way, imagery acts as both a self-diagnostic and treatment tool rolled into one.

I welcome all of you, wherever you are on your personal quest for wholeness, integration, and healing. The book is filled with a vast array of exercises to facilitate your healing journey. They are drawn from a wide variety of sources and styles — naturalistic, biblical, spiritual, abstract, concrete, and physiological, among them. <u>When you select exercises, choose those that most resonate within,</u> for as you shall see, the power of imagery rests in your rhythmic repetition of those images that engage you emotionally. It is through its daily use that you develop faith in your capacity to heal.

Reversing: The Cornerstone of Healing

If you asked me what is the single most important concept needed to understand Colette's remarkable success in healing incurable diseases, I would immediately reply: Reversing to restore yourself to wholeness.

Simply put, *reversing means making a turn in life away from habitual attitudes and distressing emotions toward new possibilities.* We go "sur-nature," or above our nature, separating ourselves and turning away from our habitual tendencies. Concurrently, we turn away from the cancer, separating ourselves from it as we do, and reverse our attitude and attachment to it.

Reversing naturally reconnects us with our most authentic

Self — that is, our higher self — and with our Source of Life. This reconnection infuses us with healing energy and provides us with a shift in consciousness.

Illness implies a lack in the sufferer's connection with the Source of Life. Rather than dealing with the symptoms, it is more effective to go to the root of the problem and adjust the situation in our mind's eye.

We have to reverse our life journey so that we can become aware of the damage imaginally, undo it, and then go forward in our life. This reversing encompasses not only our physical body but also our self-image, emotional responses, social relationships; it can even extend to the spiritual realm.

The first and simplest application of reversing refers to changing or *reversing a destructive feeling or thought* to a beneficial one or, alternatively, simply wiping it away imaginally with a pail of water and a brush.

These types of corrections are not bound to the here and now. For example, they can be done whenever you feel stressed about an upcoming event (the future) or feel out of sorts from a stressful encounter (the past). As you become proficient in imagery, you will find it easier to identify imagery that is associated with your feelings and thoughts.

A second type of reversing — *reversing our lives* — is our primary focus in the reversing of cancer. In this 12-phase program, *each phase reverses a core issue of our lives that is topsy-turvy and needs to be set aright*: our connection to heaven and earth, our bodies, "negative" emotions of anxiety, fear, and guilt, the illness and its effects, and even family relationships, present and past.

The fruit of reversing — the non-judgmental awareness as well as correction of past damage — imbues our total self with a sense of harmony, which is the backbone of healing. Through reversing we become integrated, healthy, whole human beings.

Reversing has many facets. Colette emphasized cleansing as the first step in healing. In the pages ahead, we begin by imaginally cleaning out our physical bodies. As the program unfolds we clean out destructive emotional responses, repair painful memories, correct faulty self-images, and realign ourselves with the higher self. While the relationship between cancer and a person's way of dealing with emotions has been widely researched, little medical attention — with its focus on physical interventions — has been accorded to this relationship. This is where imagery excels. Although reversing your reaction to emotional stress is a formidable challenge, imagery helps you succeed by separating you from conditioned emotional responses, even those you may have harbored since infancy.

All of us, to one degree or another, are burdened by strong emotions linked to past events or future fears which sap energy and deplete our will to fight. As you proceed, you may find yourself cleaning out long-held habits of anger, depression, fear, or guilt. Should you uncover a specific disturbing emotion or event that has not been addressed by the 12-phase program, you can find general instructions for reversing it or letting it go in Appendix B.

A third type of reversing taught here is called *nighttime reversing* — a short imagery exercise before sleeping. In it, you correct the typically repetitive, distressing emotions and conflicting social interactions of the day. The exercise not only clears your mind and helps you fall asleep easily, but also propels you forward in your healing by heightening your awareness. Colette considered it a pivotal spiritual as well as healing exercise. For those interested in it, I have included the exercise in Appendix C. It is *not*, however, necessary for the 12-phase program.

Finally, a fourth type of reversing is "dream correction." Here one imaginally reverses disturbing elements of a dream. This is best done with a clinician trained in imagery, and is beyond the scope of this book.[8]

Part of the success of reversing lies in our ability to look back at past events and relive them in a new way. We cannot change these events, but we can change our responses to them. *By reliving these images in a new way, we substitute a new memory to act as a buffer in our habitual response to a painful or traumatic one.* We don't change the fact of what has happened to us, which is impossible in any case; but we can change our memories of such facts. We can transform how we choose to remember a fact and our attitude toward it.[9]

To give you a flavor of how I work with individual clients, here is an example where a patient imaginally made a correction of a disturbing event from the past.

Joyce was fighting a recurrent cancer. I imaginally led her back in time to find the relationship between her internal distress and what had occurred the year or two before the onset of her illness. She relived the moment of waking up one Sunday morning and trying to awaken her husband so that they could go to church, only to realize he had died in his sleep.

In the ensuing months, the shock gave way to anger against

him for breaking their loving marriage by leaving her behind. The anger turned into guilt for feeling the way she did. I offered to lead her through an exercise to see herself reaching the heavenly realm through the Way to Paradise exercise found in Appendix D.

Readily agreeing, she saw a radiant bridge. With the radiance emanating from her eyes, she crossed the purifying river of fire and soared above the deep abyss. Finding herself in front of Archangel Gabriel, she asked to be allowed in the Garden to look for the soul of the one she had loved and not forgotten. A great relief swept over Joyce after she finally had the opportunity to bid farewell to her beloved. After this, she took leave of me, persuaded that her healing would soon follow.

The power of reversing is also revealed in the extraordinary story of Colette's patient, Edmund. Afflicted with what he was told was terminal cancer, Edmund visited Colette as a last chance of hope. Colette asked Edmund to visualize himself one year from the present time. He saw his own funeral, with his wife and daughter walking in procession.

Colette then asked him to do a reversing exercise looking for any difficult experience in his past. He was instructed to stop, cleanse the experience on the screen of his mind using a pail of water and a brush, and continue his journey backward in time till he reached the age of five. Along the way, he was to cleanse the scenes of difficulties, the time and place in which they happened, the circumstances, and the people involved.

Edmund then had to come forward in time, and pay attention to the changes provoked by his change of the past. When he was finished, Colette said to him: "Now see yourself three years from now." Edmund projected himself three years into the future, and said: "My wife and I have just had a baby boy. I have realized my dream to become an artist and I am having a large exhibition." And indeed, three years later, Edmund's wife gave birth to a little boy, and his creations as a painter gave him great joy.

Imagery takes you to the eternal moment of *now* — a dimensional reality beyond linear time and space in which the disease does *not* exist. You might think of it as a blueprint of your "perfect" self — whole, holy, complete, and unblemished. In this *subjective* moment, Colette focused on restoring the body's physical appearance or disturbance by repairing one's self-image. When we repair our self-image imaginally, we repair our physical bodies and restore our normal physiological functioning — we heal. For Colette, there was no split between body and mind. As she explained, the *body* is the collective unity of what we label as our emotional and physical selves — two sides of the same coin. As we restore our self-image, we restore our connection to our higher self, providing us with an influx of joy and power, essential states for fighting disease.

Dr. Epstein describes imagery as the homeopathy of the mind: a micro-input evokes a macro-response. A small dose of imagery two or three times per day can rebalance, realign, and restore you. Through small shocks, the imagery provokes the body to do its work. In this way, you learn to respond to the stresses of life in a new way.

As you imaginally repair your emotional responses, your body concurrently repairs itself — as you are a mindbody unity. You can test this mindbody connection in practice.

For example, the lab technician asks you for a urine sample but you cannot relax enough to produce one. Usually, imagining a waterfall helps your body cooperate. Conversely, when you experience "white coat syndrome" on seeing your doctor, your blood pressure rises, reflecting your nervousness.

While I have included specific imagery for strengthening the immune system and addressing particular cancers, you need not get overly focused on doing imagery to fight the disease merely on a biological level. The physical body will reflect these changes as you work through the 12-phase program, imaginally repairing your self-image, removing negative emotions, healing your relationships with others, and strengthening your life force by reversing destructive habits and conditioning.

I liken reversing to suddenly feeling hot and removing your sweater quickly, then inserting your hands into the sleeves again in the opposite direction in order to straighten them out. The problem is that it is not so easy to reverse the path of life with words alone; that is why Colette used images. As she put it: "I use words because it is the best way to have an immediate contact with someone, but images show me the inside language of the person." Bypassing rational linear thought, Colette introduced new images in a language understood by our deepest selves. These new instructions allow us to reverse our path and choose new directions.

How to Use This Book

I have divided Colette's exercises into 12 phases aimed toward healing the mindbody. The phases are progressive and are done in sequence. They permit you to gain instant access to your true Self, to cleanse all harmful emotions and to distance yourself from disease. You will learn to rely on the focused help of the mind's eye to identify and remove from within anything that you do not need, from unwanted cells to harmful emotions. The final phase in this 12-phase program helps you to see the direction in which you wish or need to grow, leaving disease behind.

There are no contraindications to using imagery. Family and friends can use these exercises, as can healthcare providers who want a firsthand understanding of the healing process, or wish to incorporate this method into their work. By traveling this 12-phase path of healing, you will undergo a transformation. You will be able to acknowledge and release the anger, sadness or anxiety you may be feeling, and know how to respond to these feelings beneficially. You will also develop the capacity to discover and create your own exercises arising from your own inner wisdom. Once you have gone through the12-phases, you continue to have the exercises available to you, whenever you need them.

HELPING OTHERS WHILE HEALING YOURSELF

While you need to be kind to yourself throughout your healing process it is important to overcome the natural tendency to turn inward and become self-absorbed. Kabbalah, the Jewish mystical path, views illness as a state of constriction where we feel separated from others and our Source of Life. In contrast, health and well-being are associated with the infinite light of the Source of Life. As part of my therapeutic work with patients, I thus encourage them to become more outwardly-directed by giving to others, particularly those suffering from the same disease. With this in mind, one of my patients started a cancer-crisis hot line staffed by patients who were already in remission. Another patient released her fear of metastasis by volunteering at a center for cancer-stricken children. Their newly acquired ability to love the being inside themselves helped express love for those around them.

By striving to reach beyond themselves, patients start the ascent to the higher awareness that brings healing. As Colette explained, healing can take place only when you separate your intention to heal from your attention.

Mentally, you set your intention to heal, do your imagery for a few minutes a day and then go about your daily business, focusing your attention elsewhere.

At the end of the book, I provide four appendices that can be used in conjunction with the 12-phase program as you see fit. The appendices are:

Appendix A: Reconnecting to Our Higher Self

Appendix B: Reversing Disturbing Emotions and Trauma, and For Women Only

Appendix C: Nighttime Reversing Exercise

Appendix D: For Clinicians — Initiating Treatment, Introductory Exercises and Repairing Relationships (for the Living and the Departed)

Chapter II

Instructions for Imaging

Imagery exercises are just words on a page until we know how to use them. This chapter teaches you how to bring the exercises to life. Anyone is capable of learning how to use them, and virtually everyone can benefit from them.[10] Imagery succeeds in direct proportion to your ability to turn your senses away from the outside world and toward your inner realm. Once you are turned inward, you can discover a mental image that stimulates your physical body. The image will come to you on its own as long as you direct your will and attention inward. If you are new to imagery, there are warm-up exercises later in this chapter. You may be wondering how imagery differs from everyday fantasies and wishes. It is easy to imagine anything in the world, but it does not mean that it is true. Secondly, if what you imagine is true, what do you do when you just see "bad things?"

These were my questions as well. Not long into my work with Colette, I discovered that when you are practicing mental imagery (closing your eyes and turning your senses inwards), you come in contact with your higher self — the part of you that knows intimately what is before you in this moment and does not lie. Your higher self is that part of you who has access to your Source of Life and is able to direct you to attain healing. The section "Reconnecting to Our Higher Self" in Appendix I provides exercises to help make this connection a reality. As Dr. Epstein explains, imagery mediates between the invisible universe — the realm of our higher self — and our present realm of awareness. Images have form but no substance, bridging two worlds.

Our perceptual senses allow us to perceive the image through our "inner eyes" instead of our usual attunement to the perceptions of our "outer eyes." What you see with your "inner eyes" can convey layer upon layer of meaning in a single image.

Fantasy and imagery are as different as night and day. Fantasy and daydreaming are repetitive, habitual ways of thinking. Imagery is spontaneous and a-historical. Unlike fantasy, imagery is not associative, and does not remind you of a previous event or memory. In other words, it is not bound by past association.[11] Sometimes when first beginning imagery, an image evokes a habitual place or memory. However, as you proceed, your imagery muscle develops, and you are able to access more and more spontaneous imagery. You may find that your imagery shifts as you continue to do an exercise over the course of three weeks and find that exercises designed for a specific use apply to other difficulties with which you are coping. This is perfectly acceptable, since mental imagery exercises have a "crossover" effect and can be used for different purposes.

What if you see something that is frightening or distressing? This manual teaches you to reverse, or change imaginally what you perceive within your inner forum of consciousness. If you are unable to correct the image, relax. You may be very anxious, caught in a spiral of fear. Keep practicing imagery. With repetition, your trust in your capacity to heal will grow. In particular, through the progressive steps of the 12-phase imagery program, you will chip away at the emotional blockages enmeshed with illness. While most people experience imagery as an inner visual perception, it is really a composite of all your senses, including sensations, feelings, visual images, and smells.

Doing Imagery

Colette begins all mental imagery exercises with the instruction to <u>breathe out three times.</u> These words are shorthand for how to sit and breathe during these exercises:

- Sit in a comfortable straight-backed chair that has armrests.
- Your back is straight, your arms are resting comfortably on the armrests, and your hands are open, palms down. If your chair has no arms, place your arms on your thighs, palms down.
- Your feet should be flat on the floor.
- Do not cross your arms or legs as this prevents the circulation from flowing. This uncrossed posture helps keep your sensory awareness focused inward.
- Similarly, sitting with your back straight allows your lungs to expand fully and promotes greater alertness. (If you are bedridden, do the exercise either sitting up, or if that is not possible, lying down.)
- Close your eyes.

- To quiet the body, we begin by exhaling rather than inhaling, as exhaling quiets the sympathetic nervous system and helps turn your attention inward.

- Do this three times: Breathe out, then in; out, then in; then out again — for a total of three out-breaths and two in-breaths. You breathe *out* long, slow exhalation through the *mouth* and a normal *in*halation through the *nose*; don't exaggerate the in-breath.

- Once you complete this cycle you need not concentrate on your breathing, and your breathing can assume any pattern that is comfortable for you. You'll find that this "reversed" out-in breathing will quickly become second nature.

If you forget to follow a breathing instruction exactly, just proceed with the exercise. When you finish the exercise, you take *one out breath* before you open your eyes.

If you like, record your imagery exercises on a smart phone, tablet, or recording device, leaving appropriate pauses between images. You can also have a friend read the exercise to you. Or, you can read an exercise and then do it with your eyes closed.

You can also find the audio version of many of Colette's visualizations, including the **Castle, Arrow** and **Key** diagnostic exercises available on my website. www.healingwithinwithout.com.

Other helpful hints: If you find it difficult to see in your mind's eye, use any of your other senses that are particularly strong. To facilitate visualization of a specific organ or body systems, find an anatomic drawing online or in a book such as *The Anatomy Coloring Book* by Kapit and Elson.

LENGTH OF EXERCISES

The rule of thumb for imagery is that *less is more:* The shorter the imagery, the greater its power. Therefore, do each exercise quickly. Aim for each exercise to take a few seconds, that is, from 10 to 30 seconds. The shorter the better. By doing the imagery quickly, you bypass the logical, rational, habitual mind, and enter the "no-time zone."

If you are not experienced with imaging or have difficulty imaging, you may need a longer time to discover an image. In such cases, an exercise may take from 30 seconds to one minute. Some exercises in this book appear to be longer than others; these are really a series of short related exercises done as a group. Between each short exercise, breathe out one time.

THE TIME FOR IMAGING

To create a rhythm to heal, try to do the imagery exercises roughly at the same time each day. I generally recommend that imagery exercises be performed at the beginning of the day before breakfast, at twilight and at the end of the day before bed. These are three potent transition points — between sleep and waking, day and night, and waking and sleep, respectively. Alternatively, you can perform imagery linked to *durable functions.* These are functions that we have from birth that we do several times a day. (For instance, eating three meals a day is a durable function.) So you could practice imagery *before* meals when you are more alert.

Prayer times are also enduring functions: sun up (or when you awaken), before sun down, and before going to sleep. They too can be linked to your imagery practice. Finally, if you miss or forget to do an imagery exercise, do it when you remember.

CYCLE OF IMAGING: ONE MONTH = ONE CYCLE

Imagery exercises are generally done for cycles of 21 days, followed by seven days of rest. This cycle parallels the biological rhythm that is present in all of us. This is most evident in a woman's menstrual cycle, which mirrors the 28-day lunar cycle. Because the imagery exercises to reverse cancer are divided into 12 phases, I have found that coordinating the phases with the 12 months of the year works well.

- Pick an exercise on the first day of the solar month and continue doing it until the 21st day of the month.
- Take a break for seven, nine, or 10 days, depending on the length of the month, until the start of the next month, unless noted in the text.
- Exercises in this 12-month program are done three times a day for the first week, and twice a day for the second and third weeks.
- On the second and third week perform the imagery in the morning and at night, skipping the middle of the day/or twilight practice.

Imagery as Poetry

The imagery exercises, like poetry, do not necessarily follow the rules of logic and may deviate from ordinary English grammar. Sometimes you may be surprised at the images that emerge and may not even understand them fully. It is not the interpretation that makes you grow, but the effect you carry within from the imagery experience. In fact, when the images surprise you, the surprise creates a light shock that provokes a healing response in your entire being, repairing your self-image and your physiological imbalances. Unlike the experiences forced on you by manipulative imagery (where you are told to feel a certain way), Colette's exercises allow you to get there on your own, when you are ready to do so.

Among the images that the program offers, choose imagery that resonates and appeals to you. For example, if you are uncomfortable with exercises in which you aggressively destroy cancer cells, simply avoid them. There are many imaginal means to remove cancer cells from your body and to empower white cells to do their work. Occasionally some of the short, sequential exercises in the 12-month program seem to repeat themselves. This repetition is purposeful and reinforces your body's innate ability to heal. Of course, you need to practice the exercise, not merely casually read it!

Record Your Significant Images

You may buy an unlined notebook to keep a record throughout each month of what you regard as the most significant images. If possible, *draw* the images before describing them in words. Your aim is to call up the images rather than understand them. At the end of the three weeks, read over what you have written and note down your responses. Certainly, if you wish, you can record your dreams as well.[12]

Warm-Up Exercises

If you are new to this style of imagery, do these warm-up exercises to stimulate your sensory awareness and enhance the imagery process. While some of us are natural imagers, others learn by practicing. Don't worry if at first you have any difficulty imaging. Imagery is a mental muscle that is strengthened as you use it. Also, you may not be noticing the images that come to you. You might be sensing something auditorily (hearing), or somatically (bodily senses), or kinesthetically (body position), yet not *see* these images. Some people respond to abstract imagery, others to concrete imagery. Some relate to imagery drawn from nature, others to biblical sources or spiritual texts. The important thing is to relax, close your eyes and let the imagery come — that is, wait for it. And when it comes, *accept it*. A single image, feeling, or sensation is enough to ignite a healing response. Whatever appears is right and can be useful even if it seems silly or impossible.

The first of these warm-up exercises — **The Bubble** — is an excellent introductory healing imagery exercise to teach you how to manipulate cells and circulation by directing the bubble as it travels all around the world. Remember to sit up straight in a chair as you do the imagery.

THE BUBBLE

Close your eyes.

Breathe out three times.

Imagine that you are drinking a glass of soda. Sense and feel the form of the glass, the coldness, the smell, and the bubbles exciting your nostrils.

Breathe out once.

Enter a bubble. Describe the texture, the colors and the sensation of lying in it; travel with it all around the world. Describe all the places where you stop.

Breathe out once and open your eyes.

FISH

Close your eyes.

Breathe out three times.

You are in the kitchen preparing fish for dinner. Feel the texture of the fish in your hands as you wash it. Season the fish with herbs and spices, and put it in the oven.

A few moments later, there is an appetizing fragrance in the air. The fish is soon ready. Serve it to your family members who are seated around the table. Hear them comment on the fish's good taste.

Sense it.

Breathe out and open your eyes.

SEASHORE

Close your eyes.

Breathe out three times.

Go to the beach.

See the blue of the sea merge with the blue of the sky at the horizon.

Feel the golden sand beneath your feet, sliding with the action of the waves.

Hear the sound of the waves breaking in the cliffs and the cry of the seagulls flying overhead.

Touch the water and bring your hand to your lips; feel the salty taste.

Smell the salt in the air.

Breathe out and open your eyes.

Part II

Healing the Mindbody

Chapter III

The Core Program:
The 12 Phases of Healing

This following program of exercises is based on Colette's teachings which, during many years of working with patients, I refined into 12 sequential phases. These phases stimulate the progressive inner movements of change that patients have found instrumental in their healing. Our aim in doing this program is to reverse cancer by setting ourselves in order. On a mental level, we shed unwanted emotions and thoughts; on a physical level, we shed unwanted cellular growth. Each phase builds on and furthers the program's basic intention by focusing on a particular theme or issue.

In addition, those with a strong spiritual perspective may choose to begin the program with the five introductory imagery exercises called *Reconnecting to Our Higher Self,* found in Appendix A. Of course, anyone may do these at any time during the program.

Phase 1 to 12 Overview

In Phase 1, we are re-rooting ourselves to life, as a tree roots itself into the earth.

In Phase 2, we listen to the messages our bodies have to reveal.

In Phase 3, we act to protect ourselves from our bodily processes which are running amok.

In Phase 4, we shift our perception of the disease from a destructive force to a cleansing light shining from Above.

In Phases 5, 6, and 7, we cleanse ourselves of anxiety, guilt, and resentment.

In Phases 8 and 9, having cleared our playing field, we are fully ready to shed the disease we no longer require. In the process, we come to know our self and rewrite our history, reconnecting in yet a deeper way to our higher self.

In Phase 10, we shift our consciousness to live at a higher plateau.

Phase 11 plunges us back into the depth of ourselves to cleanse any remaining emotional blockages.

Finally, in Phase 12, we gain the power to reach the higher aspects of Self.

I strongly recommend that you resist the impulse to skip a phase and jump to what you think you need. Trust the process and the pace. You will find this imagery quite unlike any you have done in the past. Within each phase, there are many unexpected, seemingly serendipitous twists and turns. In all, these exercises provide sufficient choice for each taste and temperament.

Selecting the Monthly Exercise

On the first day of every month (or each new phase), find a quiet time to prepare for the selection of the exercise(s) you will be do-ing during that month. There are three steps:

- STEP ONE -
Cleansing Exercise to be done only on
Day One of each new phase.

You start by doing a general cleansing exercise in order to quiet yourself and to summon your higher self to guide you in selecting the exercise(s) that most benefits you. Colette taught that the first key to healing was cleansing; she created a multitude of cleansing exercises from the simple to the complex.

Health and cleanliness are intimately connected. Just as we clean out our physical environment, we want imaginally to clean ourselves out as well.

When we clean we put things in order, ridding ourselves of things we do not need and creating space for something new to emerge within us — a new habit, a new direction, a new possibility, or a new creation.

Clear Water is a classic cleansing exercise for the beginning of each new phase — or after experiencing stress or difficulty in the midst of an exercise.

CLEAR WATER

Close your eyes.

Breathe out three times.

Imagine that you go to the kitchen and, opening the faucet, you fill a glass with clear water. Drink slowly this transparent water that quenches your thirst and purifies you.

Then delicately wash your hands and face with clear running water. Feel you are refreshed and renewed.

Breathe out and open your eyes.

Here are two additional cleansing exercises you may use as needed. You may find that as you go along you modify the exercises or create new ones spontaneously.[13]

CLEANSING LIGHT

Close your eyes.

Breathe out three times.

See, sense, and feel a cleansing light from Above penetrate your being, cleaning out whatever you do not need. Then delicately wash your hands and face with clear running water. Feel you are refreshed and renewed.

Breathe out and open your eyes.

SAND SALUTATION[14]

Close your eyes.

Breathe out slowly three times.

See yourself stretched out on a sandy beach.

See the sun above you to the right. Feel the salutary heat and the radiant light envelope you, cover you, incubate you, and penetrate you.

See yourself extending your arms towards the sun and catch the rays, bringing them back to the center of your solar plexus [the area on the front of your body just below the ribs].

Breathe out once.

Feel and sense the rays spreading from your solar plexus, which becomes the radiant center of your entire organism. See and feel these rays becoming increasingly blue, like the blue light that surrounds the sun and lights up the sky and that now flows inside you like a long and calm river, spreading its vivifying light. Feel the entire organism stimulated by a rush of life, streaming forth tranquility and joy.

Breathe out and open your eyes.

- STEP TWO -
On Day One, choose an exercise or exercises for the month.

Next, choose one or more exercises from among each month's selections. You may start with a moment of silent prayer to elicit Divine guidance. From my experience, prayer helps to draw Divine healing energy to us. The help will not always come in the way we anticipate, but it does not fail. I suggest you try at least a few different selections or even the entire monthly series of exercises, and only then decide on the one exercise or the group of exercises that resonates within you knowing that the Divine is guiding you.

Remember to do the exercises each day for three weeks. As I noted earlier, in the first week, do the exercises three times (3x) a day. In the second and third weeks, do the exercises twice (2x) a day. In the fourth week, rest completely from imagery.

- STEP THREE -
Customizing your imagery program.

Imagery is a creative process open to spontaneous change and discovery — a place where anything is possible. When practicing the imagery over the three-week cycle, you may receive images of your own which differ from the original renditions. Use these.

You may also add your own customized imagery to remove: any unwanted cell, feeling, thought, or emotion, or to address a specific tumor type, chemotherapy, or surgery. Do this at the start of each imagery session for the three-week cycle. All combined, these exercises should take no more than 30 seconds to a minute.

To Remove Unwanted Cells: Some people imagine turning on a switch or valve within themselves to enrich their immune system or turning off a switch or valve when they wish to temper an over-active immune system. Some see their bodies producing a multitude of killer T cells and interferon, which annihilate any trace of disease within. Others imagine a focused white light coming from Heaven entering them. As the light penetrates and permeates the entire body, anything that is not clean and healthy instantly leaves through the pores of the skin.

To Remove Distressing Emotions: *To remove an unwanted emotion, pain, or traumatic experience, go to Appendix B, Retracing the Past. There you will also find an exercise specifically for women to clear away any lingering emotions surrounding a past abortion.*

To Connect to Your Source of Life: *You may use Colette's favorite healing technique: See yourself ascending to the Source of all Life and becoming empowered with the healing energy you need.*

Imagery for Specific Tumors, Chemotherapy and Surgery: *In Chapter IV, you will find exercises to treat specific cancers, manage chemotherapy, and recover from surgery. If you wish, you can add these exercises to your monthly imagery selection.*

Whatever resonates within you and feels right, that is the best way of sealing any exercise with your own special healing touch. Adopt a healing attitude. As Colette said: "At first, see the good." Don't think of your illness as an enemy. Rather, see it as helping you to reach a new level of consciousness that could not have occurred without the cancer.

Tips for Getting Started

- Go from Phase 1 to Phase 12 without deviating from the order of the phases.
- Those who wish to begin with the Reconnection Exercises, go to Appendix A.

EACH MONTH

*On the first day of each month (or new phase):
- Begin by centering yourself with a cleansing exercise, and, if you wish, a prayer.
- Read over the exercises; pick one or more that resonate with you.

FIRST WEEK

- Do the exercise(s) three times a day, generally for no more than one minute each time.
- Second & Third Week
- Do the exercise(s) two times a day.

FOURTH WEEK

- Rest from imagery.

GENERAL TIPS

- If you have your own customized imagery (to remove unwanted cells, feelings, specific tumors, etc.), do it before you do the actual phase imagery.
- Modify imagery exercises to include any spontaneous images that arise.
- Reverse, correct, or cleanse away any unwanted emotions, cancer cells, images or thoughts that arise while doing the imagery.
- Refrain from judging the imagery or yourself.
- Be consistent in your practice.

POSTURE & BREATHING DURING IMAGERY

- If possible, sit up in a straight-backed chair with arms.
- Close your eyes and breathe out three times.
- Do the imagery quickly — less is more.
- When you are finished with an exercise, breathe out slowly and open your eyes.

Phase One:
Re-rooting Ourselves to Life

Choose one or more from the following exercises, most of which involve trees. Trees connect us directly to life. They reinforce their roots, sending them deeper into the ground when necessary.

DAMAGED TREE

Close your eyes.

Breathe out three times.

See, sense, and feel yourself as a beautiful tall tree with strong roots, crowned by heavy foliage. Parts of the trunk are damaged by spiders lodged under the bark.

See your tree shaken by God's Hand — or by a great storm if you are not religious.

See and know that even if the tree is cut down, it will sprout again.

You shake so violently that the damaged bark falls as do all the spiders lodged beneath. See the spiders buried under the ground.

Breathe out and open your eyes.

ORANGE TREE

Close your eyes.

Breathe out three times.

Find yourself in a garden. There is a beautiful tree with no fruit. It is an orange tree. The crown of this tree is not even. Find a ladder and garden clippers and clip off some of the branches so that it is even. Make sure that none of the branches are intertwined with another, and remove all that are not in place.

Now get off the ladder and see the oranges grow as well as more flowers. Put the ladder back.

Breathe out and open your eyes.

LEAF

Close your eyes.

Breathe out three times.

Imagine yourself in the backyard of your house. It is autumn and leaves are falling from the trees. With a rake in hand, you sweep all the old leaves into a pile and burn them. Take a small shovel and dig a hole nearby. Bury the ashes deep in the ground and with them your past difficulties.

Breathe out.

As you walk back toward the house, a golden leaf falls in front of you. Pick it up, put it in your left hand and cover it with your right hand.

Breathe out.

Sense that the heat of your hands is making the leaf return to life. Sense and feel a pulsation in your hand.

Breathe out.

Uncover it and see that your leaf is turning green again.

Breathe out.

Put it on your heart or whatever part of your body needs healing or care. and let the new life of the green leaf penetrate you, giving you sap and oxygen.

Breathe out.

Sense its freshness making you refreshed and renewed.

Breathe out and open your eyes.

FAMILY TREE

Close your eyes.

Breathe out three times.

See your family tree.

Breathe out.

Imagine that you see your place in your family tree.

Breathe out.

Sense that you are the link between your ancestors and your successors.

Breathe out.

See you and them reflecting each other, in the eloquent silence that is everlasting.

Breathe out.

Regard yourself as a shining flame without personal name or form. Give to this flame all the names of family members that you wish to include.

Breathe out.

Feel and know that nothing can happen to you that does not belong to you in your innermost being.

Breathe out.

Dive into yourself.

Once in your innermost being, plunge into the "concealed light." Find there the truth for yourself.

Breathe out.

Find what is most important for the family member about whom you are the most worried.

Breathe out.

See and sense that in the core of yourself, your mind is "stilled into silence."

Look at it. Bow in front of that splendor.

Know and see the lightning intelligence of your heart.

Breathe out.

Keep your core in its light, and sing with gladness. Hear your inside voice.

Breathe out and open your eyes.

Taking Your Life in Your Hands

Close your eyes.

Breathe out three times.

Pay attention to one of your plants, which is not looking good. Choose a larger handsome clay pot and transplant it. Feel the pleasure that comes when your hands contact the earth. Water the plant, which is now looking very strong and beautiful.

Breathe out and open your eyes.

The Lawn of Health

Close your eyes.

Breathe out three times.

See that the sun and cold weather have burned your lawn and it needs cutting.

As you push the mower, sense the refreshing scent stemming from the cut grass. See the freshly cut grass becoming very clear, bright green. Sense that you have removed what was not alive. Keep with you the fragrance of the freshly cut green grass.

Breathe out and open your eyes.

Phase Two:
Messages from Above —
The Body Speaks

In this phase, we become aware of the body's messages to the mind.

MESSAGE OF HEALTH

Close your eyes.

Breathe out three times.

Know and feel that what you accept is being delivered to you by your all-knowing mind.

Breathe out.

See, sense, and feel the top of your skull being opened. On the upper inside surface is a mailbag filled with messages. The bag is gently turned over on the crown of your head and all the mail — the messages — pour into your body through this opening on top.

The messages start traveling through your body. Quickly pick up your scrub brush and start cleaning out the different parts and dark spots of your body.

Sense that this newfound cleanliness and space are ready to receive the messages.

The messages are delivered to all the parts of your body, all corners of your being, even those you may be ignoring.

Breathe out and open your eyes.

Even if you do not read the messages, they still reach their destination in the deeper recesses of your mind. However, if you feel the need to read them imaginally, by all means do so and act accordingly.

THE CAMERA

Close your eyes.

Breathe out three times.

Imagine a camera in your hands that registers all possibilities of healing. Focus it onto the part of your body that needs healing. See that the special film inside the camera is registering all that has been difficult, bitter or painful during the past year: frustration, resentment, guilt and so on.

When the film is full, remove it from the camera and throw it into the stratosphere, knowing that the healing is done.

Breathe out and open your eyes.

FREED PRISONER

Close your eyes.

Breathe out three times.

See a lion coming out of your face. He was mastering you because you held him prisoner. Now that you have freed him, you are mastering him.

See that the parts of your body that are suffering are now perfectly healed, strong and light. See the vacant space that the lion has left in your head. You may fill it with whatever you want.

Look at the limbs of the lion. Admire them; transfer to yourself their strength and life-energy.

Master the lion; caress him and tell him to leave you alone.

When you no longer need the lion, let him leave freely and look at him leave until he disappears.

Breathe out and open your eyes.

Vicious Circle

Close your eyes.

Breathe out three times.

Step into a circle. Feel that every time you do this, a certain symptom appears. You step out of the circle and understand that there are no coincidences; the symptom occurs because it is meant to occur.

As you understand this, see that the symptom is disappearing.

Breathe out.

Step into a spiral going clockwise and see that a symptom automatically appears. You step out and go into a spiral going counterclockwise. Notice that the symptom has disappeared.

Breathe out and open your eyes.

HALVES

Close your eyes.

Breathe out three times.

Imagine that you are cut longitudinally in two halves. Sense the connection of every part with the opposite part of the brain. Sense how it acts on the part of the body that has to be readapted or reconstructed.

Breathe out.

Imagine that you fold your body in two, horizontally, every part mirroring the other. What do you see? What are you sensing? Experience how to act on the top part in order to act on the bottom part. Sense that in order to reinforce something of the top part you have to treat part of the bottom.

Breathe out and open your eyes.

GAME OF THE BLIND MAN'S BLUFF

Close your eyes.

Breathe out three times.

See yourself as a child playing blindfolded. Your hands can tell who the people are that you are catching. Put away those who are not good for you, and keep those that are good.

Then catch the suffering part of your body and remove all traces of disease.

Breathe out and open your eyes.

HEARING THE VOICE OF YOUR EYES

Close your eyes.

Breathe out three times.

See and sense your eyes as all seeing, all knowing.

Breathe out.

See and sense your eyes as life-giving.

Breathe out.

Look at your eyes in a mirror, showing vigilance, protection, stability, and purpose.

Breathe out.

Look at your eyes, not limited by the visible.

Breathe out.

Have your eyes expressing watchfulness, infallibility.

Breathe out.

See yourself with one thousand eyes; then three thousand eyes.

Breathe out.

Sense and feel the eye of intuition and the eye of higher perception.

Breathe out.

See the destructive power of the only eye of the Cyclops, and the quieting effect of the eye of the cyclone.

Breathe out.

See that your eyes are your light.

Breathe out.

See with the eyes of your heart.

Breathe out.

See into the mirror, the "Eye of Wisdom." What does it tell you?

Breathe out, and looking at this Eye, know what it is saying.

Breathe out.

See with the eyes of your soul: find and know the Truth.

Breathe out.

You are facing a blazing fire, caused by a cyclone, a powerful wind storm. Feeling drawn by the very violence of the storm, you jump in.

In the eye of the cyclone, you find a space. Inside the space, see a ray of light. Use the magnetic pull of your eyes to absorb the healing energy of the ray.

Breathe out.

You may now leave the storm, carrying within you the light and protection you need to shield yourself from the storms in your life.

Breathe out and open your eyes.

WISDOM OF THE EAR

Close your eyes.

Breathe out three times.

Sense and see your ears opened to the sounds of the world.

Hear and recognize a sound connected with your personal life, your social life.

Breathe out.

Sense and know the infinite wisdom of your ear.

See your ear knowing about something important for you and putting it into light.

Hear the music of your new learning.

Breathe out.

See yourself climbing up a hill, a bamboo stalk in your hands. Describe what you see.

Breathe out once.

With the bamboo, catch some cosmic rays coming from the sun; bring the bamboo to your ear and listen to the sounds and musical creation that come from the transformation of the light rays when they reach your ear. Recognize your own theme.

Breathe out once.

Bring the bamboo to your right ear to hear the accompaniment of the melody that you hear in the left ear.

Breathe out once.

When you reach the top of the hill, sing your song in the full light.

Know that the vision of light and your hidden treasure are always inside you.

Breathe out and open your eyes.

BLUE LIGHT

Close your eyes.

Breathe out three times slowly, and when breathing in, see the blue light coming from the sky and filling you until you become like a crystal vessel full of blue light.

See and know that this blue light is the sign of "the King bringing you into the Garden."

Breathe out once.

Know that in order to have it forever, you have to be the king or queen of yourself and transform yourself into your own Garden.

Breathe out.

Sense, feel, and know that the "Essence of Heaven" is this clarity that is in you.

Breathe out and open your eyes.

IMMOBILITY: ELIXIR OF LIFE

Close your eyes.

Breathe out three times.

Imagine yourself taking a posture of immobility.

Breathe out.

Sense and feel the physical and psychological benefit of keeping your posture. Sense the effect of immobility in combination with relaxation.

Breathe out.

Sense how the lowering of the metabolic levels of the body reduces stress by slowing and quieting.

Breathe out.

Sense how refraining from movements also has strengthening effects: bringing self-confidence, increasing will.

Breathe out.

Live and know how the suppression of movements has a liberating effect on the mind.

Breathe out.

Feel and know how accepting the leg pain that comes from long-sitting prayers calls for courage and brings self-respect.

Breathe out.

Know that this courage and self-respect — as much as full-time true activity — are taking us away from the sickness of the soul in which we experience no meaning in life.

Breathe out.

Feel and know how this attitude of the hero is the real elixir of life.

Breathe out.

Now imagine a mirror, and looking into it, see your aortic artery breathing more and more slowly until a special frequency follows its beat, traveling through the body and reverberating in the third ventricle of the brain [a sinus space in the occipital lobe of the brain].[15]

Breathe out.

Sense how the wave that is set up is traveling in the sensory-motor area, ending in the pleasure center of the hypothalamus.

Breathe out and open your eyes.

Phase Three:
Blunting the Weapons of Your Body Parts

Just as you would blunt your sword in a fencing match, so do these exercises aim to prevent your body parts from attacking your whole self. In other words, we restore our health by bringing those parts of us that are out of control back into order.

For example, on a physical level too much stomach acid leads to ulcers; in autoimmune disorders the body cannot tell foe from friend; and in cancer, undifferentiated cells grow out of control.

THE ESSENCE

Close your eyes.

Breathe out three times.

See yourself acting with courtesy. Blunt your weapons. See your weapons being cut off without leaving harmful spikes.

Breathe out.

Sense that there is a way to hold *at a distance* the drama of life.

Breathe out.

Feel and see that your drama *is not* a tragedy.

Breathe out and open your eyes.

The following exercise focuses on clearing your head.

LIGHTHOUSE

Close your eyes.

Breathe out three times.

Look at your head as a lighthouse. Look at the inner workings of your brain. Choose the functions of your brain you want to increase or energize.

See the number **1** written on the lighthouse.

See, sense, and feel how your knowledge of yourself is increasing.

Breathe out.

Now imagine a mirror, and looking into it, see the number **1** as a lighthouse. See the lighthouse focusing the light on and into the darker points of your self-image. See the lighthouse turning all around the disease and focusing on it.

Breathe out.

Look at your lighthouse as a laser that you direct on the disturbing sensations within your body. Sense the changes. Feel how you can eliminate or diminish these parts by burning the places you have chosen with the laser beam. Sense the changes.

Turn over the mirror. Look at your new sensory possibilities.

Breathe out three times.

Now, before looking at yourself, choose the parts of your body you want to increase and strengthen.

Breathe out.

Send the turning light of the lighthouse circularly all around and along these parts until you feel they become stronger or better.

Breathe out.

Look at yourself from your lighthouse. Look at the colors of your emotions and focus the laser beam to burn away the ones you want to diminish, transform, or destroy. Turn over the mirror.

Again, look at yourself from your lighthouse, and see the emotions, one by one, that you want to enrich in yourself. Shine the light of the lighthouse on them until you are feeling deeply each different emotion.

Breathe out and open your eyes.

The following exercise is done three times a day for 10 or 15 seconds before each meal for an entire three-week cycle.

PREPARATION

Close your eyes.

Breathe out three times.

See yourself as a rhythmic arc sending an arrow from source to source.

See that all the parts of the body's reality are a version-in-flesh of the soul's reality.

Breathe out.

Sense all the segments of your internal universe within the outer universe.

Breathe out.

Sense and know that to learn of the human soul and to come to know it, you need to know what your body's inside anatomy looks like.

Breathe out.

Sense and feel peace as a tranquil soul submission.

Breathe out.

Sense and feel that the study of your body is a key to the nature of God and the universe.

Breathe out and open your eyes.

Renaissance / Rebirthing

Close your eyes.

Breathe out three times.

See yourself passing backwards into a leopard skin. Sense yourself being covered by the leopard skin. See, feel, and sense all the movements, impressions, and sensations that occur. What do you feel when you remove the skin?

Breathe out.

Sense yourself being covered by the leopard skin again.

Feel each part of your body that is touching the inside of the skin.

Feel in yourself what is covert and overt (sensations, emotions, and feelings you have).

Breathe out and open your eyes.

Personal Restoration

Close your eyes.

Breathe out three times.

See and sense how, by means of the physical body, you are working on a competitive sport you like, at the best of all your possibilities.

Breathe out.

See how this form of concentration on your body is involving all your being.

Breathe out.

Sense in your body all the movements you are doing. Recognize the signal that you feel or hear when doing well.

Breathe out.

Though you perform well, still, another competitor is winning.

Breathe out.

See and feel in your body that you have your emotions under control.

Breathe out.

See and know where your error has been and experience within your body the new sensations as you perform again after the error has been cleared away.

Breathe out.

See and know that, in this way, your perfected body is now a fit habitation for your soul.

Breathe out.

Feel that you are discarding fear and desire.

Breathe out.

Know that you are expelling fear.

Breathe out.

Live that you are forgetting frustration.

Breathe out.

Sense and see your resentment pushed away.

Breathe out.

Sense and feel in your body that you have your emotions under control.

Breathe out.

See and feel all your weapons without unnecessary sheaths.

Breathe out.

Sense the freedom of disarmament of yourself and others.

Breathe out and open your eyes.

Phase Four:
Disease as a Cleansing Light

The light from the One is always there. When we prevent ourselves from receiving it, disease manifests and acts as a cleansing force to unblock us. This allows us to once again receive the cleansing light that brings joy, above and below.[16] We may use the following exercises to adjust our situation by *reversing* to reconnect with the Source of Life and open ourselves to ever increasing levels of life and healing.

CLEANSING INFLAMMATION

Close your eyes.

Breathe out three times.

Sense and see the inflammation or disorder as a big flame, a firework that cleanses the body, filling it with white light that gives joy.

Breathe out and open your eyes.

MAGNIFYING GLASS

Close your eyes.

Breathe out three times.

Hearing the inside voice — be quite sure it is yours — recognize it as a will for health and creativity and as a power to self-identity and realization.

Breathe out.

Having in hand a magnifying glass, direct the light of the sun to the diseased areas and see them burn away.

Breathe out.

See and know that good results and success are always within you, ready to be.

Breathe out and open your eyes.

CRYSTAL

Close your eyes.

Breathe out three times.

Feel and see that you are a crystal and that light is going through you.

See your new crystal shape and the rays of light shining through you.

Breathe out once.

As a crystal, listen to the different sounds emitted by the different rays that touch you.

Breathe out and open your eyes.

NEW NAME

Close your eyes.

Breathe out three times.

See yourself facing a long wall. See yourself passing through a little white door in the wall.

Breathe out.

See yourself on the other side, wearing new light-colored clothes, and see and hear yourself called by a new first name.

Breathe out.

Sense the essence of this day, of this moment, of this instant before you have been named.

Breathe out and open your eyes.

LION

Close your eyes.

Breathe out three times.

See a white lion in a cage. Know that it is a messenger of God to watch you and heal you.

See a white light all of a sudden coming down from Heaven and enveloping you. These white rays purify you and heal you.

Breathe out and open your eyes.

INSIDE THE HEART

Close your eyes.

Breathe out three times.

Open your ribcage delicately with a laser.

Carefully sponge out all the black blood that fills the heart. When your heart is empty and light, beautiful and transparent like a crystal from the Heavenly Heights, bring inside of it the image of the patriarchs, Abraham, Isaac, and Jacob. Leave them inside as long as you need their purifying and healing influence.

Breathe out and open your eyes.

CYCLONE

Close your eyes.

Breathe out three times.

See a cyclone in the center of which there is a fire. Feel the effect of its healing action.

Breathe out and open your eyes.

GRAIN OF SAND

Close your eyes.

Breathe out three times.

Hear as Abraham, "and you will be as the stars of the sky and the sands of the sea."

Lie or stand on the seashore. Have some sand in your hand.

Let all the grains of sand fall except one.

Sense it.

Keep it in your palm.

Breathe out.

Watch the grain of sand in your hand transmute into a star, then place it over your heart.

Breathe out.

See the rays of light from the star spreading out to the universe.

Breathe out.

See the rays of light returning back to the heart, which sends rays of healing through the rest of the body.

Breathe out and open your eyes.

HEALING LIGHT (from *The Bahir*[17])

Close your eyes.

Breathe out three times.

See how it is brilliant in the skies but you do not see the Light.

Breathe out.

See yourself as a crystal vessel receiving light as you breathe in.

Breathe out once.

See yourself spreading light from your crystal vessel and giving it to those you choose; to all living beings; to all other beings; and back to the Holy One.

Breathe out.

See how your name is in you, and in you is your name, to give life and Light.

Breathe out and open your eyes.

Phase Five:
Cleansing Anxiety

Phases Five, Six, and Seven focus on removing the harmful emotions of *anxiety, guilt, and resentment* respectively.

TUNE

Close your eyes.

Breathe out three times.

Keep the tune that comes to you in the freshness of the early morning.

Any time during the day you don't feel perfect, hear the tune and feel good.

Breathe out and open your eyes.

Use the following exercise as necessary to protect against anxiety or external dangers. You may also use it when you are unable to see yourself doing what an exercise asks of you.

TURBAN

Close your eyes.

Breathe out three times.

Imagine that you are wearing a white turban. As you put it on in front of a mirror, see that you look very good and feel great.

Breathe out and open your eyes.

Repeat the following exercise every day, or whenever you are not feeling well.

DANGER

Close your eyes.

Breathe out three times.

See danger facing you.

See what is saving you.

Breathe out and open your eyes.

CIRCULATION

Close your eyes.

Breathe out three times.

See your own circulation. Listen to all the sounds stemming from your blood.

Breathe out.

Look at the sky, the sun, the moon, and the other planets around the stars. See them turning all together *in the same direction* around the sun.

Breathe out.

Now you see yourself on earth, as the earth rotates around the Sun, as in a merry-go-round, in the opposite direction of the other celestial bodies. Turning with you are your siblings, parents, spouse, children, grandparents; all the people you love.

Hear the music of the stars. Listen carefully. Feel good on this merry-go-round: you are where you belong.

Breathe out.

See rays of white light coming from Heaven. The luminous rays reach the earth. You feel the impact of their force and their power as they reach the network of your veins and arteries in your body's circulation.

See your circulation coiling like a snake rolled around itself that can play bad tricks when it is not at rest.

Breathe out.

You can avoid the consequences of these "bad tricks" of the snake by visualizing the rays of white heavenly light that reach you with force as they tie the head of the snake.

The snake is now constrained in a resting position as it continues its normal function of circulation in nourishing, disinfecting, and healing your body.

Breathe out.

Look the snake in the eyes and see it transform itself as it changes skin.

Breathe out and open your eyes.

ALTERNATE EXERCISE TO IMPROVE CIRCULATION

Close your eyes.

Breathe out three times.

Imagine that your hands are very heavy because a 100-kilo weight is attached to each one of them. See the number 100 written on the weights and feel the heaviness of your hands.

You place your right hand over your heart and your left hand over the right one. The heaviness of your hands is thus transferred to your heart, which becomes very red and shiny. Your heart becomes a magnificent ruby, so precious that it is irreplaceable.

The heaviness of your hands causes your heart to circulate more effectively, so that luminous emanations stem from your hands and spread through your arteries. The blood now circulates faster in your arteries and cleanses everything that does not belong.

Breathe out and open your eyes.

THE SHIELD

Close your eyes.

Breathe out three times.

See yourself covered by a shield. See that the shield is becoming more and more transparent.

Breathe out and open your eyes.

THE ROPE

Close your eyes.

Breathe out three times.

See yourself holding a rope in your hands horizontally with four knots.

Untie the knots that are binding you. As every knot is untied, sense some of your burden is being released.

Breathe out and open your eyes.

WATER

Close your eyes.

Breathe out three times.

In the kitchen, take a very fine crystal glass and pour yourself a large glass of water. Drink it very slowly knowing that you are cleansed inside and outside.

Put the glass on the sink.

Knock the crystal of the glass and listen to the sound; keep it within.

Breathe out once.

At the tap, wash your hands and face.

Breathe out and open your eyes.

Do the following exercise for five seconds every time you feel anxious or weak.

VASE OF BLUE LIGHT

Close your eyes.

Breathe out three times.

See yourself as a blue vase absorbing blue light through all your pores.

See, sense, and feel this blue light filling you completely.

See how, as a crystal vessel full of blue light, you have a clarity reflecting the blue of the ocean, the blue of Heaven.

Breathe out and open your eyes.

PENDULUM

Close your eyes.

Breathe out three times.

See a pendulum swinging from right to left. On the right is the heap of your difficulties. The pendulum takes your worries on the right side and swings them to the left.

The way to the right is now clearer. There is more space available on the right. When the pendulum goes back to the right side, it can go farther, and in a great impulse, it takes all your worries and anxieties, now on the left, and swings them far into the stratosphere. This causes a thin rain to fall from a white cloud. Sense and feel this blessed rain cleansing and benefiting you.

Breathe out and open your eyes.

Colette emphasized that the following exercise should be done only once a year.

ANGST

Close your eyes.

Breathe out three times.

Feel the agonizing pain of anguish.

See a python slide behind you and go around you. It is turning around you, holding you tight. Little by little, it slides up until it reaches your chest. It is strangling you. It now reaches your neck.

Get rid of it by all means possible!

Breathe out and open your eyes.

ANGUISH

Close your eyes.

Breathe out three times.

Feel anguish as an agonizing physical pain.

Find a way to get rid of the pain and to feel joy.

Breathe out and open your eyes.

SQUEEZED LIKE A LEMON

Close your eyes.

Breathe out three times.

Feel the apprehension of something that has not happened yet and is disturbing you mentally.

Feel this apprehension tied in your throat, choking you, then in your heart, then the solar plexus and the stomach. Feel it as if it were a rope tied around you that burns you.

Now feel yourself embraced by someone you love, and this embrace removes what is binding you.

Wait until the rope disappears completely.

Breathe out once, and see yourself facing people who have squeezed you like a lemon. Embrace them tenderly and see that they are no longer able to squeeze you like a lemon. [If you do not want a physical embrace, you may envelop them with light.[18]]

Breathe out and open your eyes.

FIST

Close your eyes.

Breathe out three times.

Hold your hands closed in front of you. Now open your right hand and see what is inside. Open your left hand and look as well. Now change objects. What happens?

Breathe out and open your eyes.

KNOTS

Close your eyes.

Breathe out three times.

See a rope full of knots.

See and sense yourself covered by a shield.

Begin to undo the knots.

See and sense that the shield is becoming more and more transparent as each knot is untied.

Finish untying the knots that are tying you down.

Breathe out and open your eyes.

BETWEEN HEART AND THOUGHT[19]

Close your eyes.

Breathe out three times.

See and sense your heart wavering between joy and angst. Recognize and feel the conflict, and know how to deal with it.

Breathe out.

See yourself as a pendulum where joy at the right takes the place of anxiety.

Breathe out.

See, sense, and feel your heart wavering between compassion and consternation in a paralyzing serenity.

Breathe out.

See and sense how your heart is filled with fervor and horror. Find the middle path.

Breathe out.

See and feel that you may switch from exaltation to terror.

Find the way to real exaltation.

Breathe out.

Feel what it is to learn both singing and silence at once.

Experience it.

Breathe out.

Sense that you are a lamp and the lighting at one time.

Breathe out.

Sense and see yourself adaptable and holding your position well.

Breathe out.

Know that no progress is possible if you do not go out of yourself, bursting out.

Breathe out and open your eyes.

You may "tack on" the three related exercises below, or do them independently.

ADDENDUM: AGAINST YOUR HEART'S DESIRES

Close your eyes.

Breathe out, three times slowly.

See yourself doing something important that goes against your heart's feelings.

Breathe out and open your eyes.

ADDENDUM: HEART TO HEART

Close your eyes.

Breathe out, three times slowly.

Sense and feel that your heart is concretely touching the heart of someone you love and understands him or her.

Breathe out and open your eyes.

ADDENDUM: LETTING GO OF ANGER

Close your eyes.

Breathe out three times slowly.

Scream your anger to the heavens.

See how your scream is opening a space in the clouds.

A fine rain falls, cleansing all anger, and imbuing you with inner peace.

Breathe out and open your eyes.

Phase Six:
Cleansing Guilt

Of all unwanted emotions, guilt is the one that most hampers health. Colette taught that after completing the cleansing guilt exercises, it is helpful to follow up with a physical action. This corrects the wrong by making a concrete atonement or compensation.

CLEANSING GUILT

Close your eyes.

Breathe out three times.

Go backward in time, re-experiencing old emotions, identifying the feeling of guilt. Look back every five years until the time in which you were five years old, identifying the significant disturbing places and events where you experienced guilt. (You do not have to recall all of the significant disturbing places and events of your past. The specific places and events you recall are representative of similar themes.) Cleanse the scene in the screen of your mind with a soapy brush until all guilt is erased.

Breathe out and open your eyes.

GUILT WITHIN

Close your eyes.

Breathe out three times.

Experience a foreign presence inside you. See your stomach secreting the acid juice that dissolves this foreign presence within you.

Sense the foreign presence being destroyed in the small intestine and expelled in the toilet.

Flush three times.

Shower, cleansing your insides thoroughly.

Breathe out and open your eyes.

LEARNING FROM THE PAST

Close your eyes.

Breathe out three times.

See yourself looking into a mirror. Imaginally use the forefinger of your dominant hand to touch each part of your body in the mirror image that distresses you, asking:
- Toward (or about) whom am I feeling bad?
- Toward (or about) whom am I having this pain or difficulty?
- Who is the one bringing evil?
- In what bones, muscles, and organs am I having difficulty?

Touching the body as you wait for the one(s) hidden within you, say to them you forgive them and ask them to forgive you.

Breathe out.

See and know how you feel the link between your own story and your family history.

Breathe out.

See how your own relationship with others mirrors the relationship between your family story and your own story.

Breathe out.

See, live, and know how some special event that happened to your own family relates to your actual difficulties and suffering.

Breathe out.

Feel and know how the guilts of older generations are relived today.

Breathe out.

See how the guilt of not doing what was not permitted, later becomes the guilt of not having done, which then becomes the guilt of one's being.

Breathe out.

Know how it happens that we don't unveil family secrets that have been veiled for a long time.

See how the old secrets haunt us as souls without graves that keep returning as frightening ghosts until we stop talking and thinking about them.

Breathe out.

Look at yourself in the mirror. Let go of feelings, thoughts, fears, ideas, and go straight ahead.

Breathe out.

Leave all the impediments behind you.

Breathe out and open your eyes.

Should you see or sense in your mind's eye a foreign presence in any part of your anatomy, visualize a short dialogue in which you tell the presence that you forgive him or her and ask to be forgiven. Then firmly but courteously explain that he or she must leave, reassuring him or her that you will apply yourself to repair any harm that may have been committed.

The discovery of a presence points to a feeling of guilt you are harboring within yourself. When facing a lingering guilt, the question of whether you are to blame or not is of no consequence. Just remove this harmful presence. To remove the person hiding in your consciousness, acknowledge and address the feeling that has been revealed to you by the person or presence. Next, perform a genuine act of repair for the benefit of the given person.

For example, let's say that you stole an object from a person, and the person died before you had the chance to return it. A genuine act of repair could be to return the object to the deceased person's relatives. Or you could donate money to an appropriate charity in the name of the deceased. Even though an evil may be temporarily erased from the mind's eye by actions, it will come back in some form or other if not repaired in both our inner realms of consciousness and our outer shared communal lives.

If the person whose image you have seen is no longer alive, prayers for his/her soul or a charitable work done in his/her memory are satisfactory forms of repair.

STAR

Close your eyes.

Breathe out three times.

Choose a star and look at it.

See the rays of the star reaching you.

Following the rays of the star, reach for other stars.

From there look at you, here and now.

Look at each member of your family as they are, here and now, with the radiance of the star.

Make clear you know what has to be changed in you.

Breathe out once and know what has to be changed in your family or friends.

Breathe out and open your eyes.

CROSSING THE BRIDGE TO THE FUTURE (I)

Close your eyes.

Breathe out three times.

Know and see the reason you have sometimes hidden your wholeness.

Return back in time and see again some of these moments of hiding and repair them in any way you wish.

Breathe out.

Know and live that there is nothing to be acquired, only a way to recognize what is.

Breathe out.

Know how all therapeutic processes consist of discarding, revealing, liberating, or at least letting go of pain for one moment of rest.

Breathe out.

Live and know that by believing and feeling that you are your past and that you are made by your past, you are obscuring personal responsibility whereby you link your past behavior with chemical, hereditary, familial, or environmental causes.

Breathe out.

Know and live how you need less to be adjusted than to be freed.

Breathe out.

See and choose your own way to freedom.

Breathe out.

Have a blueprint of it and go ahead!

Breathe out.

See your Tree of Life. See the expanding roots. Sense whether the trunk is strong.

Breathe out.

If it is not, make it strong. Make the trunk even. See the tree full of faces, some familiar, some not.

Breathe out.

Ask the most knowledgeable face a precise and important question and hear the answer.

Breathe out and open your eyes.

The next exercise is for those older than 35 years.

Un-natural Ending: Dis-illusion

Close your eyes.

Breathe out three times.

See yourself perpetuating the old in a new situation.

Breathe out.

Sense the effort to reject the embodiment of the earlier view.

Breathe out.

See yourself stopped. Now go *through the same play* with new *actors*.

Breathe out.

Feel and live the passage by demonstrating competence from childhood dependence to adulthood independence.

Breathe out.

Feel and know that after the age of 35 comes the transition from being motivated by the chance to demonstrate competence to being motivated to find meaning.

Breathe out.

Feel and know how, to deal with change in love or work, we need patience and restraint.

Breathe out.

See and live how each passage has its own timing. Sense it resisting efforts to rush it.

Breathe out.

Live how modest actions and small changes over time are almost always more effective than precipitous or bold behavior.

Breathe out.

See and know how for inner reorientation it is necessary to make time for you alone.

Breathe out and open your eyes.

LOCALIZE AND VOCALIZE

Close your eyes.

Breathe out three times.

Look into the mirror; imagine the body-core of your identity.

Breathe out.

And into the mirror, look at your body as a whole.

Breathe out.

Imagine that you are freeing yourself of an alien resident or an intruder.

Breathe out.

See where the frustration, the resentment, and the anger reside.

Breathe out.

Sense your body from eyes to toes. Put your hands where the intruder resides. Let the sound go out.

Looking at your body in the mirror, locate in what part of your body your energy resides and hear it.

Breathe out.

Feel where your joy resides and where love resides.

Tell them to fill all of your body and your being.

Let them sing the song of life.

Feel and see yourself increasing in size when hearing this song.

Breathe out.

Let yourself return slowly to your normal size, and stay with your song of life.

Breathe out and open your eyes.

Phase Seven:
Removing Resentment

As a prerequisite to health, one of the challenges we each face is letting go of resentment. Bearing a grudge, tucked away in your body, states that something other than the Divine or Higher Power has the ability to affect your well-being. Conversely, by letting go of a grudge you are acknowledging that the injustice you suffered came from a Higher Source — not from the hand that executed it — with the purpose of helping you grow beyond yourself.

By accepting the suffering, you experience an awareness of its lofty provenance. You thereby elevate the suffering back to its Source on High and open yourself to receive a renewed flow of life force from the space of total healing. If you cannot forgive another, part of your consciousness remains connected to the offender: Forgiveness allows you to let go.

In addition to the following exercises, you may follow the ancient wisdom and pray for God to forgive the one you resent for the harm s/he has caused you. Then pray for God to release His compassion toward you and your loved one. Forgiveness will follow.

LOSING FACE

Close your eyes.

Breathe out three times.

Look at yourself in the mirror. See your face is disappearing.

In a circular motion, clean the mirror from right to left.

Turn the mirror around. Reconstitute the face with the pieces of puzzle that fit.

See the face smile.

Breathe out and open your eyes.

FACIAL EXPRESSION

Close your eyes.

Breathe out three times.

Look at your face in the mirror. Think of someone that you resent.

Look at the expression on your face.

Turn the mirror around. With your finger, trace the changes in the mirror to make it change.

Breathe out.

Then look at it. If you are pleased, leave it. If you find that it has become too soft, change it again.

Breathe out and open your eyes.

The next exercise "Natural Ending by Crossing the Bridge" is made up of five sections. Feel free to limit yourself to one or more exercises.

1. **DIS-ENGAGEMENT**

   Close your eyes.

   Breathe out three times.

   See yourself withdrawing from your customary life routine.

   Breathe out and open your eyes.

2. **DIS-IDENTIFICATION**

   Close your eyes.

   Breathe out three times.

   Live the loss of what you think you are.

   See yourself with new eyes.

   Breathe out and open your eyes.

3. **DIS-ENCHANTMENT**

   Close your eyes.

   Breathe out three times.

   Live the discovery that someone or something dependent upon you is not as you thought.

   Breathe out and open your eyes.

4. DIS-ORIENTATION

Close your eyes.

Breathe out three times.

Feel and see yourself losing all sense of what to do when dis-oriented.

Feel and see yourself losing all sense of what to do when losing your actual self-image.

Breathe out and open your eyes.

5. DIS-ATTACHMENT

Close your eyes.

Breathe out three times.

Enter a room through a white door. The room has six mirrors: one on each of the four walls, one on the ceiling, and one on the floor. First look at yourself to the left, then to the front, right, back, up, and down.

In any reflection, if your face shows resentment, push the image out of the mirror to the left with your left hand.

Breathe out and open your eyes.

Phase Eight:
Detaching from Disease

In separating from the disease, you come to know your higher self.

Disease on Stage

Close your eyes.

Breathe out three times.

See the disease or disorder on a stage, a little higher than yourself.

See the different parts of your body in a discussion with the disease.

Sense the distance between the disease and you, increasing it slowly until only the light remains.

See clearly what is happening on stage. Discover in that space what's new for you.

Breathe out and open your eyes.

Dialogue

Close your eyes.

Breathe out three times.

Imagine a dialogue between yourself as a child and yourself as an adult. Listen to the questions and answers of both.

Breathe out and open your eyes.

Do the above exercise for seven consecutive days, and see the child growing a little every day, until adulthood.

EVERYDAY CONFLICTS

Close your eyes.

Breathe out three times.

Imagine an image inside of you.

Breathe out and see the image outside of you. Have the image of the inside say something to the image of the outside. Have the image outside say something to the image inside.

Is there some sort of struggle? What meaning are you getting from these images?

Breathe out.

See yourself as small as a sesame seed. What is happening?

Breathe out once.

See yourself as small as a poppy seed. What is happening?

Put the poppy seed in your hand. Look at it until something happens. Then put it or its transformation into your heart. What is happening?

Then put the seed or its transformation between your eyes. What is happening?

Breathe out and open your eyes.

Body Trip (1)

Close your eyes.

Breathe out three times.

See yourself as you are looking at yourself into a mirror, looking from different angles. View all the parts and then the whole.

See and know that by looking at your own image from different angles you are reconstructing yourself and the cosmos.

Breathe out and reconstruct the child that is passing in you.

Breathe out.

See yourself kneeling near a pond.

Look at your face in the water; then look a second time two feet farther away; and then see a third face in between.

Breathe out and open your eyes.

Body Trip (2)

Close your eyes.

Breathe out three times.

Looking at your body, examine the core, and imagine your flesh overflowing as a fruit, growing and growing around the core.

Breathe out and sense how you become greater and greater, until you are immense, growing above all habitual limits. Be aware of all the new sensations.

Breathe out.

Reverse your movements to look now at the core from the outside of an enormous flesh balloon. From this place, contemplate your body and know who you are.

Breathe out three times and return slowly to your natural size.

Breathe out.

Look at an object you like that you habitually caress with your eyes. Imagine that this object is looking at you.

Breathe out.

Bring yourself to the place of this object you like. Become the object. Now look at your own body from the place of that special object. Look at your body with all the feelings of warmth and pleasure that you usually give this object.

Breathe out.

Have someone you love standing in the place of the object you are fond of. Now change places with this loved one, and as you stand in his/her place, be under his/her eyes' warmth and care. Take the time to look at you and to find what it is in you that you usually don't see. Look at your body inside and outside.

Breathe out.

From the top of a house look at your self descending the back staircase of the house. Know how all of what you choose to be is contained in your bodily form. See yourself complete and perfect, climbing up the front staircase of your house, rejoining your apartment, entering your bedroom, and sleeping quietly in your perfect form.

Breathe out and open your eyes.

REVEALING YOURSELF TO YOURSELF

Close your eyes.

Breathe out three times.

Look at a bunch of rays of light, each one forming a hand when reaching the earth.

Follow the life of each one of them.

Breathe out.

Live the life of one particular hand.

Breathe out.

See the person living this life regenerated and healthy.

Breathe out, and physically open your eyes. With your eyes open, see what the person living this life is doing in the future with his/her new health.

Close your eyes.

Breathe out.

Know how your mind is the cycle of death and birth.

Breathe out.

See yourself in the desert, where the Great Pyramid is, and look at the smile of the Sphinx.

Breathe out.

What is it telling you?

Sense and know that all the images that are sent to you are a way of revealing yourself to yourself. Be happy with what you are.

Breathe out and open your eyes.

CLEARING CONFLICTS: THE WAR WITHIN

Close your eyes.

Breathe out three times.

See the first conflictual image that comes to you.

Describe it clearly to yourself.

Breathe out and see how it makes itself present in your life.

See an opposite image to the first one.

Breathe out and compare the two images noting the outstanding differences between them.

Breathe out.

See these two opposite images come together in unity, knowing now that a repair has been made.

How do you feel?

Breathe out and open your eyes.

VISION

Close your eyes.

Breathe out three times.

See, sense, and hear that: "The ears are not satiated from hearing, nor the eyes from seeing."

Breathe out.

See, sense, and hear that vision is, "to rise in thought." Live the teaching that "one who gazes into the vision" first descends and then ascends.

Breathe out once, and at first, look down from above.

Breathe out three times.

Imagine yourself lying with a tall mirror standing at your feet.

Have the image in the mirror join your lying image, making one image of light in the form of a laser beam.

See this image of light leaving your body ascending into the sky to see the earth from the moon.

See this image of light looking down at yourself.

With this "laser-beam" of light, what do you see in yourself that you have not noticed before?

Breathe out.

See this image of light looking at one person you love or like.

Breathe out.

See this image of light look at one person you dislike.

Breathe out.

See this clear image of light above you look at a difficulty in your life.

What is happening now?

See what is most important for you.

Breathe out and open your eyes.

CHANGES

Close your eyes.

Breathe out three times.

Imagine that you are a salmon climbing upstream in a torrent of water towards its birthplace in the mountains. See it making its jump above cliffs and waterfalls. See and feel it exhausted but happy, reaching the goal of her birth-place where she lays her eggs.

Breathe out.

Imagine you are a scarab beetle going out of its hole and pushing up in front of you a ball made from earth, grass, and seeds.

See the scarab beetle between a brook and a hill, obliged to climb up the hill, striving not to lose the ball that is becoming bigger and bigger.

Breathe out once.

See the scarab beetle (that is you) reaching the top of the hill, and see far away the goal that the ball has to reach to have its seeds sprout and grow.

Breathe out once.

Now that you see the goal, let the ball roll down the hill.

Breathe out as you let go of the ball.

Return to your own form, extending and elongating your body. Begin by the tip of the toes and all the articulations and muscles of the legs and thighs, all the spine bones and adjacent back muscles, and all the hand and arm bones, shoulders, and neck.

With your arms up, have your face and palms horizontally placed to face the sun.

Let the sunlight and warmth fill all your body outside and inside.

Take the sun in your hands and touch each part of your body.

Return to your own size. Stay dressed with light or in a light color.

Climb down the hill, reaching the bottom. Climbing up over the torrent, bend and wash your hands and face and drink, drink, drink (slowly).

Breathe out and open your eyes.

Phase Nine:
The Winds of Change

This phase is the culmination of Phase Eight in which you separate from the disease and completely distance yourself from it.

FOUR WINDS OF SPACE

Close your eyes.

Breathe out three times.

See and sense how the four winds blow at first slowly, gradually becoming stronger and then very strong to allow you to breathe out the physical difficulty.

Sense the disease being detached delicately by the sweet winds and being swept away by the stronger winds.

Breathe out.

When it is done, breathe out and see and sense in yourself your light-bearing soul who has left you during the time of impurity.

Breathe out.

See and feel that it is returning and filling the cleansed area. Sense being complete and fully alive.

Breathe out and open your eyes.

THE CONCEALED LIGHT

Close your eyes.

Breathe out three times.

And know many don't see the Light, even though it is brilliant in the sky! The one who walks on the wings of the wind.

Breathe out.

Feel and know that you are the one who walks on the *wings of the wind*.[20]

Breathe out.

By accepting uncertainty, feel that you have released your capacity for freedom. Live how you are appreciating this, and sensing your own power.

Breathe out.

Feel in you this truth coming from the process of change.

Breathe out and open your eyes.

SPIRIT FROM THE FOUR WINDS

Breathe out three times.

See and feel as Ezekiel did when God takes him suddenly in His own hand and brings his mind to see the large plain filled with dry bones.

Breathe out once and hear the promise, "I shall fill you with My breathing."

Breathe out, and hear the promise, "You shall return to life."

Sense the bag of dried bones on your shoulders, and know what they are for you.

Breathe out.

Breathe out on these bones and make them alive.

Breathe out.

Sense that the breathing is entering them and that they are returning to life, and they are getting up.

Breathe out.

Feel, know, and hear the words, "I shall put My spirit within you and you shall live forever."

Breathe out.

Know in yourself who and what is speaking and acting within you. When you know this, hear it, and see it again and again.

Breathe out and open your eyes.

REVERSING HISTORY: BREAKING THE IDOLS

Close your eyes.

Breathe out three times.

Hear, as Abraham, the injunction *"lech lecha"* [laych luh-cha] — "go to yourself."

Breathe out.

Feel awakened, renewed, renovated, resurrected.

Breathe out.

Be challenged, as Abraham, by the one "unsurpassed trial."

Breathe out.

Live, as Abraham did, breaking the idols.

Breathe out.

Feel and know in yourself the total change and the newness when breaking away from your accepted way of life.

Breathe out.

Hear and see Abraham telling God, "*hineni*" [hee-nay-nee] — "Here I am, I am coming now."

Breathe out.

Hear, live, and feel the reverberation of the sound "*hineni*."

Breathe out.

Live and know how the sound "*hineni*" is the key that has opened the fifty doors of the Palace.

Breathe out.

Live and know how by crossing the bridge, you are passing the Red Sea, jumping over the abyss, reaching the source of the river, walking on the wings of the winds.

Breathe out.

Know and sense all this as a potential that is now reality. Feel that it is already present in you, always with you.

Breathe out.

See and choose your own way. Have a blueprint of it, and go ahead.

Breathe out.

Sense how all in your life is welcome and how you are teaching yourself to laugh because life is simple and you are smiling at it.

Breathe out and open your eyes.

Phase Ten:
Living as Vibration —
Meeting the Wonder of Life

See living as a harmonic vibration of the body that produces a joy that raises you above yourself. As Colette said: "Living is vibrating."

LIVING AS VIBRATION

Close your eyes.

Breathe out three times.

See and live that you are feeling your body and your entire being.

Breathe out.

Live and recognize your own joy.

Breathe out.

Recognize it as the scintillating sign that you are on your way. Know that this way is the right one.

Breathe out.

Feel this joy as the vibration of the body, of the heart, of the mind.

Breathe out.

Sense that the joy you experience is elevating you to Spirit.

Breathe out.

Sense that this joy is of the same quality as that of the naive one, or of a young child, or of the fullness of the true lovers.

Breathe out.

Feel and see this joy as a promise of life. Know that this eternal joy is only of the instant.

Breathe out.

Feel and know how this instant of joy is the marvel of life.

Breathe out.

Sense that it is raising us above ourselves.

Breathe out.

Feel its wonder.

Breathe out.

Feel and know how discovering the "hidden marvel" of the instant of joy is the reason for all forms of quests.

Breathe out.

Sense, feel, and know how everything valuable begins with the body and by jumping out of the body.

Breathe out and open your eyes.

LIVING: "LISTEN TO THE MUSIC OF THE LIGHT I HAVE GIVEN YOU"

Close your eyes.

Breathe out three times.

Live your brain as the organizer of all your sensations, emotions, and feelings, and as the means to have your impact on the outside world.

Breathe out.

See, sense, and know that your mind works like an arrow on a single track to a pointed goal.

Breathe out.

Feel your body as a harp vibrating under the different events of your life.

Hear your inside music. Hear each disharmonious distrubing event of your past become harmonious within you.

Breathe out.

Feel and sense that you are creating all these changes and are making them living, responding, and resounding.

Breathe out.

See and feel all your being as one and undivided, radiating, sending all you have conquered to the world and to others.

Listen to the music of the light that you are emitting.

Breathe out.

Hear and see yourself as a pianist who at the same time is:

- o Reading the part
- o Hearing what you are playing
- o Paying attention to each hand
- o Observing the conductor's baton
- o Making the audience feel what you feel

Breathe out.

Dance undivided by being one.

Breathe out.

Hear, feel, and know that you can only give to others your music if it is truly your own and you are not playing a role. Hear and feel yourself living the truth while singing and dancing.

Breathe out and open your eyes.

Phase Eleven:
Descending into the Self
to Cleanse Emotions

Descending in your imagination takes you to the depth of your Self. There you can identify and cleanse harmful emotions. You go down to cleanse harmful emotions, and you go up to see the direction in which you want to grow. When you step down or up in these exercises, the movement is concrete, i.e., sense and feel it happening within you.

PASSING THROUGH

Close your eyes.

Breathe out three times.

See the disease passing through the space between two pillars.

Breathe out.

See the disease passing through the space between sea and foam.

Breathe out and open your eyes.

GENERAL RETURN

Close your eyes.

Breathe out three times.

See yourself descending a ladder, staircase, or rope.

Stop every five steps and notice your feelings and emotions at each interval.

What do you see when you reach the bottom?

What is happening?

Breathe out and open your eyes.

ALTERNATIVE DESCENT

Close your eyes.

Breathe out.

Swimming on the foam of the sea, you find a cave below. You go down, stopping every five steps.

What do you see when you reach the bottom?

What is happening?

Breathe out and open your eyes.

KNIGHT OF ARMOR

Close your eyes.

Breathe out three times.

Imagine that you are carrying all the weight of your sickness on you like a metallic armor. Nothing can rid you of it. Some-one tells you that if you can gain access to the Garden of Eden, there is a little lake where, at the junction of four rivers, the water is so clear that it cleanses everything.

Breathe out.

In spite of your heavy armor, you are walking towards the Garden. Leave the place where you are and go into a valley. On one side, you have a cliff; on the other, you can see the ocean at a distance.

Breathe out.

You are now walking on a very narrow path bordered by a wall. Over the wall, you can see beautiful trees of different scents. A very pleasant fragrance is stemming from the trees.

Breathe out.

You have now arrived at the entrance of the Garden. You are facing a very large gate.

You try to open the gate but cannot. You are now very tired because the weight of your heavy armor is exhausting you. The armor is, in fact, so heavy that you begin to have difficulty breathing, and so you decide to remove the helmet.

Breathe out.

Take it off and throw it behind you. Now decide to remove the armor from your body and arms; throw them over your shoulder.

Now that your arms are free, you feel much better, and you want to free your legs. You begin by freeing the knees, and after that, you remove the pieces covering your calves and thighs. Throw all the parts over your shoulder.

When you remove the boots, you are completely light and agile. You then go to the gate. Your hand is ready to open it. If the door opens on its own, go through and say "thank you." If it does not, open it yourself. Describe to yourself what you see.

Breathe out.

You are now walking on a very smooth path, and looking for a body of water.

Breathe out.

Describe to yourself what you see.

Dive down into the water, staying under the water for as long as you can hold your breath.

Go back up to breathe and go down again, staying under the water for as long as you can hold your breath.

Go back up to breathe, and on your third descent into the water, look at the bottom of the water to find something that is there for you. Take it and keep it for yourself.

Breathe out.

Ascend out of the water. What are you wearing now? How does your hair look? Now choose a tree that appeals to you and sit underneath. Look at the living beings around you, the animals in the Garden, the insects, the birds.

Breathe out.

Now look at what you have brought up from the depths of the water. Know what message it is telling you. You become whole again and feel yourself at a higher level, beyond the level of time and space.

Breathe out.

Take a walk around the garden. Look at the flowers. Fill yourself with the beauty of the garden.

Now leave the garden and go to rest at the edge of the sea. Sit there and rest near the sea while you watch the joy of the children on the beach. Look at the beauty of the ocean and the infinite sky.

Breathe out and open your eyes.

FAMILY ALBUM

Close your eyes.

Breathe out three times.

In front of you is a family album. Start looking at the last page. Which are the last pictures in the album? Who is in the picture? What are the events they show?

Breathe out and open your eyes.

HATRED[21]

Close your eyes.

Breathe out three times.

Imagine that you are at home, in your bed. You get up. Close to your bed there is a staircase going down. You go down the steps and arrive in a large space with a very soft light; it is lit with the glow of the jewelry you are wearing.

Breathe out.

You reach a green meadow. On one side, there is a small forest, and on the other, a very light brook. Walk on the bright green grass full of flowers. Sit among the flowers. Listen to the sound of the water and to the soft wind whistling among the trees of the woods.

Breathe out.

Pick some flowers and press them against the parts of your body that need healing. You feel the flowers are communicating all the vitality and energy from their sap which renews the energy and vitality of your organs.

Breathe out.

When the flowers have given all their sap and are withering, you throw them in the river. Then you drink slowly from this water which is crystal clear. Feel that this water is cleansing you and giving you inner peace and serenity.

Breathe out.

Feeling peaceful, you wash your face and hands in the brook. Now you start walking back to your room by the way you came. Filled with energy, fix your bedroom. Put everything in order and change things you have not changed for a long time until you feel it is more harmonious.

Breathe out.

Dress yourself in light-colored clothes.

Breathe out and open your eyes.

BANNER

Close your eyes.

Breathe out three times.

There is a long white wall in front of you. In the middle of it is a small door.

Breathe out.

Open it and see an intensely black space that shows the most profound depths.

See a banner come forth that is solely there to protect you, as you say to yourself "And Your love is a banner on my head."[22]

Breathe out.

Walk forward a few steps. See that there is a pit and a ladder. Go down to the bottom. Who is there?

As you come back up, see the banner on your head and sense that it is also your shield and your sword.

Breathe out and open your eyes.

In this phase, we attempt to cleanse the emotions that are held deeply in our consciousness. Consequently, in the exercise above, if you find a monster in the pit, first look it in the eyes, realizing that it has no power to harm you, and then bring it up from the pit with you. See what it looks like in the light of day, and then discard it.

Should you find a relative, thank him or her for being down there, and ask him or her what he or she has to say to you. Then, as you did before in "Learning the Past" in Phase Six, firmly but courteously explain that he or she must leave, reassuring him or her that you will apply yourself to repair any harm that may have been committed.

The discovery of a presence points to a feeling of guilt you harbor within yourself. As I noted earlier, when facing a lingering guilt, the question of whether you are to blame or not is of no consequence. <u>You must remove the presence</u> — for it is harmful. To remove the person hiding in your consciousness, acknowledge and address the feeling that has been revealed to you by the person or presence. Next, perform a genuine act of repair for the benefit of the given person.

HIDDEN IN THE WELL

Close your eyes.

Breathe out three times.

The Sacred Wisdom is hidden in the depths of a well.

Breathe out.

Now draw it up from the well and see what message this holy wisdom offers you.

Breathe out and open your eyes.

Phase Twelve:
The Power to Ascend

These exercises ignite a powerful impulse within us to initiate our ascent in the direction in which we yearn to grow.

LADDER

Close your eyes.

Breathe out three times.

You find yourself facing a very high ladder whose top you cannot see. You want to climb, and yet you are too heavy.

At every fifth step, you stop and get rid of what is burdening you.

Breathe out.

You finally reach the last step. What happens? What do you feel?

What do you understand? What do you see and hear?

Breathe out.

Now that you have reached the top where everything is light, bring the light down with you.

Breathe out.

When you reach the bottom, you no longer need your old clothes. Make a hole in the earth at the bottom of the ladder and burn them. Then cover the hole with earth.

Breathe out.

Keep within yourself the impression you felt when you reached the top.

Breathe out and open your eyes.

Visiting the Ancient Toledo Synagogue[23]

Close your eyes.

Breathe out three times.

Find yourself at the entrance of the ancient synagogue in Toledo, Spain.

Breathe out.

See some poor and sick people passing by near the door. Some beggars are sitting outside.

Breathe out.

Notice that the floor and ceiling of the synagogue are covered with luminous circles that are intertwined.

Breathe out.

See the high, red double ladder in the center of the room that reaches the luminous ceiling.

Breathe out.

See the old, sick, and ugly paupers dressed in tattered clothes climb the ladder, one by one.

See them transform themselves when they reach the top.

See their clothes become light colored, clean, and beautiful. As they are climbing, see them adopting an alert and carefree attitude.

Breathe out.

See them reaching the top of the ladder, their heads close to the circles of light of the ceiling.

See how they become young and beautiful when they read what is written there.

Realize that you are able to read the Hebrew inscriptions carved into the walls and ceiling.

Breathe out.

See the people on their way down the ladder, having become intelligent and happy, as well as beautiful and clean.

Sense yourself covered with purity and white linen.

Breathe out and open your eyes.

CARS

Close your eyes.

Breathe out three times.

You are taking a walk up a narrow path, with the sea on one side, a mountain on the other side, and the sky above. On the mountainside, you see a junk yard of old cars.

Feeling good because of the beauty of the landscape, you are filled with love for everybody you know. See the cars being fully repaired, one by one, and following you.

Breathe out and see that your clothes change and your inside is repaired.

Breathe out and open your eyes.

Inspiration

Close your eyes.

Breathe out three times.

See that you are standing on your white horse in the middle of the desert. You have a dream, and you pray in your dream to know what you have to do and which book you have to write.

Breathe out.

See that you are standing on your horse at the top of a hill in Jerusalem. You are looking all around, filled with the Presence.

You sense the Presence; you know the Presence. You want to be nearer. You feel extremely alive with all new energies. Hear and write the words of God.

Breathe out and open your eyes.

Past, Present, Future

Close your eyes.

Breathe out three times.

See a wall in front of you with three doors. Go to the one on the right and open it. See what or who is inside.

Go to the center door. Open it.

Go to the left door. Go inside three steps and look around.

Breathe out and open your eyes.

Crossing the Bridge to the Future (II)

Close your eyes.

Breathe out three times.

See yourself climbing down a mountain cliff until an abyss stops you.

What are you feeling?

Breathe out.

Construct a bridge over the abyss, using any material that you wish.

Breathe out.

And now, pass above your own bridge.

Breathe out.

Climbing down a mountain, you are in a hurry, but you are stopped by a torrent. No time to find a bridge. Put a white turban on your head and climb up and jump over the torrent. Where have you jumped to? What is on the other side? What are you doing there? What are your feelings?

Breathe out.

See and feel how, by accepting the risk and the uncertainty, you have released your capacities for freedom and are sensing your power.

Know and feel how, by facing death, you are accepting the unknown.

Breathe out.

Know how this potential that is becoming a reality is already present in you, always within.

Breathe out and open your eyes.

When this book was in its final stages of editing, I visited a relative on the Sabbath. Unfamiliar with the living quarters, I tripped and fell extremely hard. I went to sleep while still in shock from the experience. When I woke up a few hours later, I cautiously touched the painful spot on my chest and realized that while the right side of my collarbone was perfectly smooth to my touch, the left side seemed to be cracked. Indeed, the skin was red and swollen outside.

Like the proverbial shoemaker who has no shoes, I am not good at visualizing. However, since this was the Sabbath and the effects of my fall were not an emergency, I did not seek medical help. Imagery was the only option.

I thought of imaging white light coming down to heal me,

but when I actually closed my eyes and started imaging, Colette's teaching came up: "No, no! You must go up to the light, not bring it down to you!" I saw myself going up, slowly, with determination. As I was getting closer to the top, my clothes changed into a beautiful white garment.

The closer I came to the top, the more the powerful energy of love and care enveloped me. This light was perfect and complete. It was Divine Unity, and everything coming in contact with it was affected. My bone instantly healed. After this visualization, my collarbone no longer hurt, and ceased to be the focal point of my attention.

Chapter IV

Stepping Out of Fear and Worry

When you engage in any process, the process itself gains momentum within you like a rolling ball gathering speed in its course. The process of worry is no exception. A major element in the stress of cancer is the worry of recurrence which may spiral into a circle of constriction unless stopped in its inception, or even better — before it begins. When we battle cancer, and even after we have won the battle, we often find ourselves worrying about cancer's return. This is particularly true the days or nights before a scheduled checkup. Our job here is to rid ourselves of the fear and worry when these emotions appear.

Throughout this book I have tried to transmit Colette's message to sufferers: *You can step away and detach yourself from the condition; stop yourself from identifying with it. You and the cancer are not the same!* Similarly, you can detach yourself from your worries.

THE STRANGLEHOLD OF WORRY

Close your eyes.

Breathe out three times slowly.

See the fear or worry of a recurrence strangling you like a noose, and either ease it, loosen it, or remove it from around your neck. Notice then how your breathing improves, and at the same time know that your worry has evaporated.

Breathe out once and open your eyes.

Sometimes as we lay down to sleep, our worries tumble in upon us. Below is a simple nighttime reversing exercise you can do to rid yourself of your worries. Do this exercise for 21 days in a row, or whenever you can't sleep. It may be done together with each of the twelve phases. As you continue to practice this, you may be able to sense an emerging worrisome or fearful thought immediately *prior* to its occurrence *during the day* and eventually stop these thoughts from occurring.

BEDTIME WORRIES

Close your eyes.

Breathe out three times slowly.

Relive your day by going backward in time, recalling any moments of worry or fear you experienced during the day. Upon encountering such a moment, you may wash it away to the left with a bucket of clear water, or correct the memory in any way you wish. When you have corrected the images, breathe out one time, say "worry gone" and sense your body relaxing as you fall into sleep peacefully.

FOR FEELINGS OF OVERWHELM

Close your eyes.

Breathe out three times slowly.

See, sense, and feel yourself removing your burdens – the fears, worries, cares, and activities that overwhelm you. Place them in a black trash bag. Burn the bag with a great torch until only ash remains. Bury the ash deep in the ground. Sense how light your body becomes. Notice how your breathing deepens as the body becomes lighter, knowing that your burdens have been removed.

Breathe out once and open your eyes.

CHASING AWAY THE CLOUDS OF DOOM

Close your eyes.

Breathe out three times slowly.

See your fears as dark grey clouds overhead. Take a golden pen and draw a circle of light. Enter the space you have created. When there, breathe out imaginally three strong out breathes (in between each out breath take a normal in breath), seeing the dark grey clouds above you pushed away to the left and evaporating.

Breathe out.

Now feel and sense the restoration of your strength growing with each breath, separating you from the clouds of fear, and reconnecting you to your higher self. Know that you are making your way back to unity and wholeness.

Breathe out and open your eyes.

Some worries and fears feel so entrenched in our beings that they seem to have taken residence in our bodies. We feel constricted, tight, tense, and knotted in these areas. Here is an exercise to remove these constrictions.

EMBEDDED WORRIES AND FEARS

Close your eyes.

Breathe out three times slowly.

Scan your body from head to toe, sensing and feeling where you have tucked your worries and fears away.

See your hands and fingers becoming translucent and very bright, and your fingers becoming very long. Gently remove each care and worry and toss it behind you far away. Sense and feel your entire body relaxed, radiating health and joy.

Breathe out once and open your eyes.

Chapter V

Exercises to Reduce Specific Tumors

In this chapter, I provide exercises for specific tumors, a general anti-cancer exercise, as well as exercises to help you through chemotherapy, radiation, and post-surgical recovery. You may do any of these exercises by themselves for one to three cycles before taking a break, or you can add them to the phase on which you are working. The rule of thumb is to use an image for no more than three cycles (that is, three months) before you take a month's break from that imagery.

If you are undergoing a radiation and/or chemotherapy regime, you may find that your will is too depleted to concentrate fully on the imagery program. If so, here are some suggestions:

- Stop doing your imagery program on treatment days/ weeks, but resume the program during the off treatment days/weeks.

- Stop doing your imagery program during treatment days/weeks, but continue to do one cleansing or anti-cancer exercise during the rest periods between treatments. Do it three times per day, and if possible, for three weeks (21 days) at a time.

- You can always do the **Turban Exercise** during the on-treatment days/weeks.

EXERCISES FOR SPECIFIC CANCERS

Brain (1) Cleansing to Heal

Close your eyes.

Breathe out three times.

Wash your hair with shampoo and lots of sparkling water. If any section of the hair is not bright enough, see how the light from Above makes it shine.

Delicately cut around the circumference of the head. Remove the top of the cranium carefully as you would remove the top of a round box. Using your hair, gently sweep away all the old emotions, guilt, and feelings of resentment.

When it is clean, put the top back gently and glue it carefully with a blue-golden gel. Then wash your hair once again.

Breathe out and open your eyes.

Brain (2) Removing a Tumor

Close your eyes.

Breathe out three times slowly.

Imagine that you have in your dominant hand a laser scalpel of light. In your other hand, see a tiny eye at the end of each fingertip. With the laser scalpel open the top of your skull circularly as you would a box. Remove the top and place it in a sterile box.

Look at the brain and see the place of hurt. See that it is not so large. Using the laser, cut away the unhealthy part and throw it very far behind you.

Breathe out once.

With the five eyes of your hand, scrutinize your brain. If you see a color that doesn't please you, cut off what has to be cut and scoop away what has to be scooped away.

Breathe out once.

Look at your brain; with your two hands, take hold of it and put it in a sterile box. Now clean the part of the skull that stayed on your shoulders. Gently take the brain in your hands. Caress it very delicately and say: "You are learning to live a new way, full of health and light."

Breathe out once.

Put your brain back where it belongs. See and sense a blue light-glue emerging from all your fingertips that you spread around the top of your skull. Gently, put the top of your skull back in place. See a circle of blue light around your head that now actively prevents headaches.

Breathe out once.

Sense that the malaise has disappeared and you feel much better.

Breathe out and open your eyes.

You may also use **Visiting The Ancient Toledo Synagogue** (Page 127) or **Lighthouse** (Page 60) to heal brain tumors.

Breast

Close your eyes.

Breathe out three times.

See a ray of white light entering your chest.

Feel immense love and compassion as the white light spreads within your chest.

At the contact with this light, anything that does not belong within you leaves through the pores of your skin.

Breathe out and open your eyes.

Colon

Close your eyes.

Breathe out three times.

Gently take your colon and turn it inside out washing it in a crystal clear glacial stream. Have with you a golden brush and wash away all the impurities — both physical and emotional — that have been stuck to the colon. When it is gleaming whitish-pink, turn it right side out and return the colon to its proper place in you.

Experience how your newly purified body, free of waste matter, allows you to connect to your higher self. See how this connection prevents any blockage in your colon.

See, sense, and know that this connection grants you the inner wisdom to select and consume healthy nutrients that support the colon and allow for effective eliminations.

Draw down this connection to higher self into your daily awareness.

Breathe out and open your eyes.

Bone Marrow: for Leukemia

Close your eyes.

Breathe out three times slowly.

Hear your own voice saying the verse in Hebrew from the Book of Ezekiel (37:7), "*vatikrevu atzamot etzem el atzmo*" [Va-tic-re-voo ah-tza-mote eh-tzm el ah-tz-moe] — "and the bones came together, each bone to its matching bone."

Breathe out.

See how your bones are formed: The end of each healthy bone(s) touches the end of its leukemic bone(s).

See the bone marrow flowing from the healthy to the unhealthy bone(s).

See the unhealthy bone(s) revitalized.

See and sense the white and red blood cells streaming forth

from the revitalized bone marrow into circulation. The white cells are rivers of radiant white covered with gold; the red cells are rivers of bright red covered with blue.

Breathe out and open your eyes.

Do the above **Bone Marrow Exercise** for a period of 21 days, twice a day, for 30 seconds each time; then rest a week. Resume the exercise twice a day, for 15 seconds each time, for another 21 days. If possible, always do the exercise before meals, along with an exercise from the phases.

Liver

Close your eyes.

Breathe out three times.

Become very tiny and enter your body through the cavity of your mouth. Your hands are full of light. The fingers of one hand have little hands at their extremities. The fingers of the other hand are endowed with eyes.

With these eyes, look inside your liver and notice what is not perfect inside; now, remove what should not be there with the tips of your fingers.

Light is streaming from both of your hands so you see very well what you are doing.

When you are finished, look again to make sure that all is clean.

Breathe out once and leave, the way you came.

See, sense, and feel clear transparent rain fall and cleanse you inside and out.

Breathe out and open your eyes.

Lungs (1)

Close your eyes.

Breathe out three times sensing your lungs becoming very bright and heavy.

At the same time, your heart becomes as heavy as a precious stone, a ruby. The ruby sends light all over the body.

See, sense, and feel your body filled with a very shiny red light streaming from the ruby, as your body becomes very heavy.

Know that this light has eradicated anything that does not belong in your lungs.

Breathe out and open your eyes.

Lung (2) Embryo

Close your eyes.

Breathe out three times.

See, sense, and feel yourself as an embryo. See your stomach cloning itself and flipping over your diaphragm to rest in your chest.

Breathe out one time slowly, and see this new stomach split vertically in two, each piece becoming a new lung and jumping into place around the heart.

Sense your new healthy lungs performing their new function perfectly in preparation for a new way of breathing oxygen at birth.

See yourself as a perfect newborn human being.

Breathe out and open your eyes.

Ovaries

Close your eyes.

Breathe out three times.

See and feel how a renewed flow of life force is pumped into the space of your ovaries, restoring the gift of life.

Breathe out and open your eyes.

Skin: The Peach of Immortality

Close your eyes.

Breathe out three times.

Go to the garden and see a peach tree. Admire the beauty of the peaches. Select the most beautiful one.

As you hold it in your hands, pay attention to its color and feel its silky texture. See it grow and grow. Then look at all its defects now magnified. Cut them off.

Then see it return to its original size and put it back on the tree.

Breathe out and open your eyes.

GENERAL EXERCISE FOR ALL TUMORS

Healing Light (from *The Bahir*[25])

Close your eyes.

Breathe out three times.

See how it is brilliant in the skies but you do not see the Light.

Breathe out.

See yourself as a crystal vessel receiving light as you breathe in.

Breathe out once.

See yourself spreading light from your crystal vessel and giving it to those you choose, to all living beings, to all other beings, and back to the Holy One.

Breathe out.

See how your name is in you and you are in your name to give life and Light.

Breathe out and open your eyes.

Exercises for Chemotherapy and Radiation

Do the following exercise daily before leaving home for chemotherapy or radiation treatment.

Turban: For Protection

Close your eyes.

Breathe out three times.

Imagine that you a wearing a white turban made of silk. As you put it on in front of a mirror, see that you look very good and feel great. Know that the turban protects you throughout the treatment.

Breathe out and open your eyes.

The Waterfall: To Wash Away Toxins

Close your eyes.

Breathe out three times slowly.

Imagine that you are in a friend's home near a private lake, naturally surrounded by a hedge of thick bushes.

Entering the lake, sense that the water temperature is just right. Wade forward, going toward the waterfall at the opposite end.

Breathe out once.

Place yourself under the waterfall. Sense and feel the water washing down over you with gentle strength. The water penetrates deep within you through the pores of your skin. See the toxins from radiation and chemotherapy as a black substance that is washed out of you leaving through the soles of your feet.

Breathe out once.

Feeling cleansed, step out of the waterfall and pronounce a prayer of thanksgiving. As you do, see a ray of white light coming down from Heaven and penetrating you as it completes the healing action of radiation and chemotherapy.

Breathe out once.

As you emerge from the water, sense a new growth of hair in your scalp. Feel how the waterfall has cleansed you within and without.

See Divine light surrounding you.

Breathe out and open your eyes.

To Heal from Radiation Burns

Close your eyes.

Breathe out three times.

See yourself ascending a staircase of clouds. Feel the coolness on your skin.

Breathe out once and feel a deep relaxation reach all your body parts.

Take a pale beam of moonlight and direct it to your burned

skin. Sense the coolness of the white rays as a healing balm on your skin. See how the burned skin becomes paler and paler every time you breathe out. Sense that all traces of burn ebb away at the contact with this healing light from above.

Breathe out and open your eyes.

To Shed Nausea

Close your eyes.

Breathe out three times slowly.

See a staircase in front of you whose steps are painted in different colors. The first step of the staircase is the deepest color. As you ascend, the step colors become lighter and lighter. With each step up, feel the depth of the color and hear a sound for each color. Feel how you shed some of your nausea with each step you climb.

What happens when you reach the top of the staircase?

Come back down, bringing your experience with you.

Breathe out and open your eyes.

See also, on page 150, **To Restore Health** exercise, for symptoms of Nausea.

To Remove Treatment Side Effects (*adapted by Rachel Eyal*)
Close your eyes.

Breathe out three times slowly.

On your right side there is a pendulum, swinging from right to left.

On the right is the heap of your side effects: fears, pains, nausea, hair loss.

The pendulum takes your side effects on the right side and swings it to the left.

The way to the right is now clearer. There is more space available on the right. As the pendulum goes back to the right side, it swings further back, and in a great impulse takes all your side effects, now on the left, and propels them far into the stratosphere.

Ask the hand of the One to complete the purification of your difficulties, bringing you light and joy.

Breathe out and open your eyes.

POST-SURGICAL EXERCISES

The intention of the following exercise is to remove the residue that sometimes remains after a cancerous tumor has been surgically removed. Colette suggested that the exercise be repeated twice each for 21 days, resting seven days between cycles. The first time with the intention to remove the residue, the second time with the intention to remove any trace of residue.

To Remove Residue

Close your eyes.

Breathe out three times.

Imagine a white flame coming from Heaven penetrating inside of you and going throughout all your body, purifying everything.

The flame then leaves your body through your mouth and rises back to Heaven and there bursts into magnificent fireworks of all colors.

Feel your body completely purified of the residue. Pronounce a prayer of thanksgiving.

Breathe out and open your eyes.

To Restore Health *(Based on a poem authored by an unknown African-American poet)*

Close your eyes.

Breathe out three times.

Hear the voice of the water, the water who is speaking to the earth, and that the fire is hearing.

Breathe out and hear the fire telling the wind where to go.

Breathe out and feel the wind who is moving the bush; hear the song of the bush resonating as the soul of nature.

Breathe out and feel the song that whips the blood — the rhythm that chases away anxiety.

Hear this song and sense all your life in your blood.

Sense how all nausea, pain and fear ebb away from you as you breathe in the soul of nature.

Breathe out and open your eyes.

Chapter VI

The Flame of Hope

For the past months, we have devoted ourselves to the daily practice of imagery. I have encouraged you to act on any insights you have received by repairing, where possible, any difficult relationships with others.

Sometimes, despite our commitment to get well, we see no improvement. We may despair and come to believe that we suffer senselessly. Compounding this, we find that our habitual dispositions — such as fear, doubt, and despair — have magnified under the stress of the illness. In these situations too, we can use imagery to reverse these feelings and thoughts, minimize pain, and relax. The key remains to *detach* and *distance* ourselves from the cancer and destructive emotions and thoughts.

I recall the exercise Colette gave me when I faced the challenge of writing this book. "Get out of yourself and go to the top of a near tree. From there, look down and see yourself writing. Then read what you are writing." In a similar way, you can step away and detach yourself from the condition; stop yourself from identifying with it. You and the cancer are not the same! Similarly, you can detach yourself from your fears and the physical pain you may be experiencing. In a sense, these exercises allow you to relinquish your *suffering* — literally what you are *bearing* — and to make a leap in consciousness to a higher plane.[26]

In the **Releasing Fear** exercise your aim is to leave behind constricting emotions and find yourself at peace with whatever the future holds for you.

RELEASING FEAR

Close your eyes.

Breathe out three times.

See and live the fears, regrets, frustrations, resentments, and sufferings at the difficulty of making decisions that have pushed you into emptiness and loneliness.

Breathe out.

See and live how these fears are fear of the unknown and fear of death.

Breathe out.

See, feel, and know how to fight against these fears — to take yourself out of the time-space duration of everyday life we call horizontal reality.[27]

Breathe out.

Now go into such an intense present that it is lived as a vertical eternity.

Breathe out.

See, feel, and know that to live the intense present in a vertical eternity, we have to change the duration of the past inside of us.

Do it by keeping the intensity of the present as a fully lived past.

Breathe out.

See yourself constructing the vertical line instant by instant. See each instant as a point.

Breathe out.

See and feel how you are living one point after another as a fully lived life.

Breathe out.

Feel and sense that this fully lived life makes you, at each point of the vertical, newborn again in the eternity of the present.

Breathe out and open your eyes.

The following exercise helps you to let go of pain by coming out of yourself and ascending to your personal Source of Life. Through your ascent you may perceive a higher truth where pain is no longer relevant.

LETTING GO OF PAIN

Close your eyes.

Breathe out three times slowly.

In your mind's eye see a part of your body feeling pain.[28]

Imaginally place your hands on this body part. Your hands feel very heavy as if weights were attached to them.

Sense as this heaviness from your hands is transferred to this body part, you feel more and more and more relaxed.

The knot of pain is unloosened, thread by thread, wave by wave, until it is totally undone.

Breathe out once slowly.

This deep relaxation of your body part then spreads to your entire body, and from there all around you, breaking open the capsule of pain that had surrounded you.

Breathe out once slowly.

The way is now clear for you.

Your inner being soars upward.

Basking in the light, above all pain and burden, you trust.

Breathe out and open your eyes.

The real you is this being of light created with the innate ability to leave the suffering body behind and ascend to draw strength from your Source. Actualizing this potential is also one of the first lessons I learned.

After studying Torah all night I had laid down briefly to rest. Suddenly I was caught in a whirlwind, but I was somehow able to pull out and get up: I was feeling so light! I remember verifying with amazement that all my fatigue had vanished. I then looked down and there was my body, lying on the bed.

But the "real me" was floating near the ceiling ... I went through the walls, outdoors, and floated over the trees, feeling perfect peace and harmony. Abruptly, the thought came to me, "How on earth am I going to get back to my body?" In that instant, I was back.

Of course, what happened to me then was an out of body experience, which happens in dreams and imagery as well. In this manner, each of us can ascend at any moment to another reality, leave behind the prison of illness and pain, disengage from the state of constriction below and draw strength and perception from the light Above.

Through imagery, Colette taught us to come out of the suffering body and ascend to the Source of Life. In this realm of healing grace you are able to cast out your burdens onto the One and become renewed.[29] The following lines are part of a compendium of poems composed by Colette toward the end of her life.

Pulled up by your prayer —
I am lifted to a space
Of absolute quietness.
There I am returned
To primeval unity.
Having reached totality
You bring me back
To my own place.
In this new state of Unity.

Renewed, I am all again,
And perfect —[30]

Asking for "the right thing"
To be done,
We put it
In the hands of the Divine,
For "His will" to be.[31]

As a young poet sung:
Thank you for my trust in You
So I know You know what's best,
So I do not fear the times
When You put me to the test.[32]

In my view, our struggle is a gift that has enabled each of us to release the bubble of anger, fear, and doubt, and reconnect with the immense love of the One. In the lofty space of trust, we may accept that even if we do not understand why we experience disease and pain, or why babies have to die at infancy, we know inwardly that what we endure — the individual as well as the collective — is accomplishing a higher purpose and helps to bring light and healing to our fragile world.

Trusting does *not* mean resigning ourselves to die. On the contrary, we must keep the flame of our hope of recovery burning. For how long? As long as there is breath on our lips. We may do the following exercise when we believe ourselves to be in danger, meaning that we don't see any improvement in our condition despite numerous efforts.

Use this exercise when you believe you are in danger.

LIGHT ILLUMINATING YOUR ROAD

Close your eyes.

Breathe out three times.

See and know how for you, now, in the instant of creation, obscurity is also clarity.

Breathe out.

Live how our function and duty is to find these words of light: "Let Your words be the lamp that is clearing my steps, a light that radiates on my road."

Breathe out.

I said to a man who stood at the Gate of the New Year: "Give me a light that I may enter safely into the unknown," and he replied, "Go out into the darkness, and put your hand into the hand of God. That shall be to you better than a light and safer than a known way."

Breathe out.

Hear and see the injunction from the prophet Isaiah: "Get up straight into the light. The Light of God is surrounding you. Its Eternal glory is here."[33]

See, feel, and sense it.

Breathe out and open your eyes.

The Horizon Exercise is for family members and friends when they believe you to be in danger:

HORIZON

Close your eyes and breathe out one time.

Taking the hand of the ill person, see his/her facial expression.

Walk slowly into the horizon until you have walked so far that you are mere points on the horizon.

Breathe out one time.

Turn around and walk back until you both return. See the new expression on his/her face.

Breathe out once and open your eyes.

From a spiritual viewpoint, there is a purpose to every second of life we each are given on this earthly plane. Even in witnessing or experiencing intense suffering, our intention is never to shorten the gift of life.

LETTING GO

For some, remaining in the material plane no longer seems to be an option, but they still feel the pull of earthly ties. I would like to share a beautiful example of the process of letting go.

Rose's father was in the final stage of terminal cancer. After praying for her father and singing to him until she had little strength left, she prayed that the Ultimate Healer would help her find the words of comfort her father needed to hear. She sensed her father wanted to go but was not allowing himself to leave his human form. The years rolled back in her mind and she remembered a story he had told her time and time again about the life changing moment of seeing the Land of Israel for the first time. He arrived in Israel as a refugee in the early fifties from an internment camp in France after having been imprisoned in Egypt for five years.

"It is just like when you arrived in Israel, Daddy," Rose said "remember when you described the cold and dark and disorientation of the ship. You left all you knew and could not imagine what was ahead. Do you remember feeling such fear even though you were supposed to be going home? Well, it is the same now. Just as you could not have imagined the sweetness and relief of seeing the Land of Israel at dawn, soon you will be home at ease, and all of your doubts and fears will melt in an instant when you know you are home."

After Rose reminded him of this story, she could see a visible change in him. He now had a luminous, beautiful peace and calm about him. Two minutes later his pulse suddenly dropped as his loved ones were gathered around him.[34]

Another example of 'letting go' was told to me about a hospice volunteer visiting a woman in the last stages of a terminal illness.[35] The volunteer asked the woman how she was feeling.

"Scared," she answered.

"Let us think together," said the volunteer. "Tell me, what kinds of things make you happy?"

The woman thought for a moment. "Balloons," she finally said. "Balloons make me think of my childhood, of birthdays…"

"Then, whenever you feel scared, think of balloons and let go of all concerns," suggested the volunteer.

The next day, the volunteer found the nurse crying when she came to the hospital ward. "What happened?" she asked.

"After you left, I went to see our patient and I could not help noticing how happy she looked. I tried to speak to her, but all she said was 'Balloons, balloons!' A few hours ago, I went in again, and…she was no longer. She had such a happy expression on her face!"

In her case, the image of balloons and its association with childhood happiness was all she needed to disconnect from the discomfort of her body and switch to a state of consciousness imbued with peace and harmony. In this state, she was able to accept that she had fulfilled her function in this body and was ready to go beyond its limitations, reaching a state of pure being. In the case of Rose's father, it was the image of his first encounter with the desired Land and his yearning to be there — as Colette expressed it, "Jumping to catch a sparkle of eternity."

THE HAND OF GOD

Close your eyes.

Breathe out.

See yourself in the Hand of God.

Breathe out and open your eyes.

Part III

CELEBRATING LIFE
A Tribute to Colette

Since we are half way,

We can change what is above like what is below.

It is the same game on earth like in the sky.

We are able to change the course of events instantly,

What happens and what is to happen.

—Colette from Mea Culpa

Chapter VII

Colette: A Life of Giving

For more than 50 years, thousands of people from all over the world walked down peaceful Shimoni Street in Jerusalem to stop at a bright blue gate. They would go down eight stone steps, cross a small patio with hanging plants, and enter what looked like a nineteenth-century North African retreat but was in fact a modern three-room apartment. The people had come to Colette Aboulker-Muscat to be healed of incurable diseases, neurological disorders, depression, even possession. Colette dedicated her time to helping them, without remuneration, out of her love of God and humanity. Let us peek into one of these healing scenes:

An eighteen-year-old girl sits on a bright orange cushion surrounded by ivory inlaid tables and an aura of ancient splendor. The walls above her are covered with oversized tapestries, Oriental hangings, and nineteenth-century oil portraits. Facing her is a petite woman in her eighties, who radiates serenity and authority.

The girl, Sara, suffers from acute anorexia nervosa. It

began a year before, when her grandfather died, and she started to feel detached from life. Colette asks her to close her eyes, breathe out slowly three times, go back in time, and search for where she had experienced the same emotions before. As she goes backwards in time through her teens and childhood, Sara keeps saying "no." Suddenly, she stops and recalls a similar moment in time.

"I am five years old," she says. "I am at the beach with my parents and some other families. The children are building sand castles. Mine is the most beautiful of all, and I want to show it to my father. I run to him, but he is talking to friends. 'Let me finish,' he says. A few minutes later, I see the tide rising. I go back to him. He gets angry with me. 'Stop interrupting me!' he shouts. I go back dejected. As I watch my castle being washed away by the tide, I feel I am disintegrating together with my castle. I do not want to speak to anyone ever again."

In the ensuing conversation, Colette learns that since that incident Sara had spoken rarely, only confiding with her grandfather. After the latter died, Sara no longer spoke. As Colette probes into how her grandfather's death evoked such violent emotions in Sara, the girl lets go of her past.

Colette asks Sara to relive the moment in which her grandfather died and she decided she no longer wanted to speak with anyone. Colette instructs her to cleanse the scene as one would clean a television screen — the episode, the people involved, the time, and the atmosphere. She is then asked to go backward in time until early childhood, identify

each time she felt a similar type of disintegration in her past,
and cleanse each scene in the same way.

Sara opens her eyes. Colette asks her husband to bring a
tray of food. Sara begins to eat.

The seeds of Colette's technique were sown in early child-hood. At the age of four, Colette was stricken with an ailment of the vocal cords. Her father, a famous neurosurgeon, decided that the best therapy would be to keep her from speaking by covering her mouth with a bandage that would only be removed to allow her to eat or wash her face. When he was called upon to serve his country during World War I, he requested that the bandage remain in place until his return.

Although he saw Colette during his years of service, he did not remove the bandage because the vocal cords were not yet healed. For four years, the little girl learned to watch, to dream, and to grow. Her imagination developed, complementing her inability to use the faculty of speech.

Reading her autobiography, *La Vie N'est Pas Un Roman,*[36] one sees the origin of many of her most beautiful imagery exercises, insights, and inspirations emerging from her childhood spiritual inner-visions and journeys. She described a "game" of imagination that she played with her beloved foster brother Gabriel and her other cousins on seeing the first star of the night sky that marked the start of a holiday:

That evening Gaby and I with some older cousins receive the
Star. The first star appeared behind a very large tree. It is one

of the oldest and most beautiful trees in Oran,[37] We are all sitting on the steps, our faces raised in the same direction. As soon as I see the Star, each one of us sits up and attempts to find his way to her, from within. We forget the traffic in the street, the screams and laughter of the children in the garden and from the other side of the park.

And I "see" that the white staircase where we are sitting climbs up the Tree. And we also climb. The white marble staircase, which has become transparent, takes us up to the Star. On the Star, we are all sitting, attempting to capture its rays, its twinkle, its beauty, and with all our hearts, we send forth our armfuls of light to someone we love below... Each one of us picks up the light he has left from the star and makes himself a mantle with it. Each one of us descends lightly, as if slipping down the large alabaster translucent staircase, each wearing his shiny clothes. Each one of us brings back home with him his own little bit of sky for his loved ones.

I come down last; Gaby is in front of me. We are transparent. We are two small white flowers, which come together at times and are at times separated. From all the cousins preceding us, descends — in the shape of fireworks —a beneficial rain, which will water the gardens and the families.

Gaby is now a beautiful calm light. I am so small that there is nothing left of me. So narrow, that I no longer hold anything. Then I become a shining point that bursts in a flare. And I turn, I turn around the earth. I am the comet of our birth.[38]

From an early age, Colette learned to prepare for each holiday by "living it" in images. This was not an escape to an ivory tower of fantasy, but her inner voyage to sacred realms.

From a young age, she began to use images to help others. The gift of healing that would make thousands flock to her Jerusalem residence could already be seen in these early years as she helped the war-wounded recover through her technique of visualization. She was six when during WWI, on the festival of Passover, her family received news from the front.

> *That night, we receive a telegram. Grandmother offers a short prayer before opening it. We are all around her to know who is wounded, who is killed, maybe. Grandmother opens the telegram with her oriental letter-opener. They have to amputate my father's gangrened leg [as the doctors were not able to preserve it]. Consternation invades us. Nobody talks. Grandmother has us pray all together.*
>
> *I "see" Maman [mother] lean over Papa's leg and clean the gangrene with her beautiful white hands of a pianist. She tears the gangrene off with her nails. She starts at the thigh and ends towards the foot. I see Papa's leg lighten up. The only thing I have left to do is to come near him, and with my hands lightened by Oran's sun, fill papa's leg with light. Papa comes out of his coma, gets up and walks. His veins are carrying pure blood!*
>
> *The same night the gangrene disappeared from Papa's leg: they will not amputate. His veins are carrying pure blood!*

This vignette shows Colette healing her father at a distance. First she "sees" what his condition is; she then "sees" her mother cleaning out the wound, and finally Colette fills the wound with the bright penetrating desert sunlight of Oran and "sees" him healed and whole. Time and space cease to exist in this non-dimensional realm.

Colette believed that each of us has the ability to reconnect to our Source. This connection is not time-bound, but is alive in each of us — individually and collectively, through the generations, both past and present, in the eternal moment of now. In this moment of no time, healing of self, others, and the world can take place. So, for example, during the festival of Shavuot — celebrating the giving of the 10 Commandments and the Torah at Mt. Sinai — Colette related this inner journey as follows:

[My] grandmother tells the children to "imagine that you are Moses on Mount Sinai. You are with all the [Israelites] of that time, grouped in a spiral around Mount Sinai. Together with them, you hear the Word."

I "see" a very large rainbow roll around the mountain. Moses has his arms raised in a great blue flame. The rainbow is made of all the colors of all the men who form it. I recognize them. Gaby is holding my hand, but we are traveling in the rainbow. Our fathers and our cousins, our uncles and all the friends who are at war are [here right now]. I see my father with his stretcher-bearers go around the battlefield on his white horse. I see the soldier whom they have just brought back near a burning plane. I see them observe the blue fire surrounding Moses and, like him, receive the Word that they listen to. I see Uncle René who has forgotten Moses, but who is listening to him. I see Grandmother Chou telling a story to her grandchildren. I see each one of the children become a grandfather or a grandmother, telling the same story to his/her grandchildren. Each one of them listens to the Word. Each one of them is at Sinai with Moses. I see the grandchildren of my grandchildren — they are smiling at me. I am well.

I see Uncle Raymond in a trench, praying. He also can see Moses' flame at that moment. He also is on Mount Sinai at the same time. He also hears and understands everything that his future grandchildren see at the same time, as well.

As a child, Colette often traveled with her mother to the war front to see her father. As she visited her father's patients, her empathy for human suffering was awakened. In an attempt to alleviate their pain, she began using techniques of healing through imagery that she had thought of during her enforced silence. Since her mouth was bandaged, she would write the patients little notes asking them to do exercises.

One of the exercises was to imagine white snow, sparkling like diamonds, which would be applied to their wounds. They were then to "see" their skin perfectly healed.

She also devised a technique to help wounded patients who were in shock. She would ask the patient to imagine that his size shrunk until he became minute. He was then to "see" himself entering himself through his open mouth and descending to the site of the wound, his way lit by the glow of his fingertips. He was then instructed to thoroughly cleanse the wound of any internal bleeding or coagulated blood. Somehow, the direct confrontation with their wounds helped patients recover from shock.

Her devotion to others was imbued by her maternal grandmother, a direct descendant of the renowned Torah scholars Rabbi Shlomo ben 'Aderet (*Rashba*) and Rabbi Yitzchak bar Sheshet (*Ribash*), who in turn descended from King David.[39] As the eldest grandchild of the Sheshet line, Colette was taught from the age of six that she would have to earn the twelve-hundred-year-old family crown by becoming righteous like her ancestors. She had duties toward mankind, and fulfilling them would bring her happiness. If she fulfilled her duties, she would receive the crown on her eighteenth birthday. Colette did indeed receive the crown, an elaborately shaped silver plaque, 90 centimeters high, topped by a silver headdress, and surrounded by a long veil embroidered with silver sequins. She donated it to the Israel Museum.

During World War II, Colette became a heroine of the Resistance in Algeria (1940-42). The leader of the resistance movement was Colette's brother, Josie Aboulker, and the majority of its members were North-African Jews. According to historians, the Allied landing in Algiers on November 8, 1942, which saved the Jews of North Africa from the Nazis, was made possible by the zeal of this group. Colette was honored with two Croix de Guerre as well as a Croix de Resistance for her work.[40]

After the Allied landing, the director of the Military Hospital in Algiers asked Colette to comfort dying soldiers. She treated her first cancer patient, a prominent middle-aged French gentleman who had cancer in his knee. Closely watched by the hospital personnel, Colette gave him several calming and healing exercises. The patient entered remission and lived fifteen years longer, dying of unrelated causes.

Colette later developed these childhood gifts by formally studying both visual imagery — the language of the spirit within — and sculpture — the outward form. Her work in sculpture achieved such perfection that prior to her leaving sculpture to devote all her efforts to imagery, one of her clients bought her entire collection sight unseen.

On one occasion, while she was in Paris, her father asked her to get him some urgently needed information from Professor Henry Baruch, at the Psychiatric Hospital St. Maurice, located just outside Paris. The professor received her in the hospital's beautiful garden, which sloped gently toward the river Marne. Colette questioned him about a group of fifteen patients standing passively on the side. He explained that they had come out of concentration camps and were suffering from "camp disease"— they lived in a stupor, totally silent and passive.

Suddenly, Professor Baruch was called away by an aide. Promising to return in a moment, he left Colette in the garden. She began to observe the passive group. Using her knowledge of morphology — the art and science of face reading — she judged from the lines and shapes of their faces that they were probably not Jews. On impulse, she started to sing carols. The effect was overwhelming: the patients began to sing with her!

A sharp cry caused her to turn around. There stood Professor Baruch, beside himself in amazement. "What did you do to them?" he asked. "For months we have been trying to get through to them without success!"

The professor insisted that Colette stay and help four young women of the group who were in labor. Medical examinations ascertained that their babies were ready to be delivered, but the women's complete lethargy led the professor to believe that they did not want to give birth because the babies had been fathered by Nazis.

Colette was hesitant, because at this point her work was purely intuitive, but she agreed to meet one of the women. She spoke to Carla in her soft, melodious voice until the young woman was able to let go of her tension. She then asked Carla to imagine herself in God's hand and to let go. The guided imagery profoundly touched the young woman, who burst into tears and spoke for the first time after years of trauma and pain. "It must be true that God loves me because He brought you to me!" Carla was then able to give birth.

Subsequently, Colette studied psychology at the Sorbonne. She completed her required internship in imagery studying with Robert Desoille, who specialized in having people dream while awake.[41] Her sessions with Desoille took place at his home, after midnight; for that was the only time he could give her. Desoille had done extensive research and writing on the subject of imagery and had gone so far as to study psychiatry privately in order to confirm his theories. Desoille learned from Colette as much as Colette learned from him. She disagreed with Desoille's practice of intervening in his patients' images by asking them to visualize him helping them whenever they encountered a difficulty in their images. Colette intervened in her patient's images only when there was an imminent danger to the patient's mental health. She stressed the importance of not intruding on an individual's free will.

Toward the end of her doctoral studies in psychology, Colette worked as the only therapist in an organization that facilitated emigration to Israel. She was able to occupy the position single-handedly because of the speed of her guided imagery techniques. During this time, Colette also began to experiment with sound therapy. She referred to the new techniques she devised as "clef-cloche" (bell-key), because a bell's ring provoked a small shock in patients, which opened new possibilities in healing. Reversing the Pavlovian method, she used sound to de-condition people.

After the war, Colette taught psychology and imagery for seven years at the University of Algiers and worked in the Psychiatry Department of the Great Hospital of Algiers, where, as an example of her innovative genius, she utilized music on the psychiatric wards. She would bring her own phonograph and records and select the piece most suitable for each patient she treated. While working mostly in Algiers, she would spend four months a year in Paris.

Along with her extensive knowledge of medicine, particularly neurology, acquired from her father, she developed a profound understanding of mindbody unity and applied it to the imagery process. The University of Geneva became interested in her work in imagery and invited her to earn a doctorate in the subject.

Colette married very young, gave birth to two sons and later was divorced from her husband. When her youngest son was twenty and Colette was just about to receive her doctorate, she married a professor of law and moved with him to Jerusalem.

Her new husband objected to Colette's receiving a doctorate. For the sake of domestic tranquility, Colette acquiesced. However, she could not have been more at the center of public interest had she received the degree.

Colette's sharp intellect and uncanny knowledge of people blended with her loving-kindness to others. She gave all of herself without ever asking for anything in return. For instance, she did not allow herself the "luxury" to do visual imagery in order to relieve the sharp back pains plaguing her, for, as she said, "each therapist has the risk of confusing his dreams with those of his patients. This is all the more true with images, which are very powerful. If I did visualizations, I would not be able to distinguish between my images and those of my patients or students, and thus be unable to help them." Colette felt that the imagery she would receive for herself could impact the imagery she gave to the patients in ways not optimal to them.

Another example of her kindness among the multitude I recall: An exhausted 87-year-old Colette at the end of a long morning of work did not hesitate to tell an anxious mother with a six-year-old who was struggling with the so-called "Attention Deficit Disorder" at the beginning of his school career: "Bring him over right now. I will give him an exercise that will help him focus his concentration. Never mind my rest; it is urgent to help him at the very beginning of the school year."

The exercise that Colette gave the child was to draw a circle each day before going to school and place a dot in the middle of the circle and then breathe out three times. Throughout the school day, he was to keep a mental image of this circle and dot whenever he wanted to focus on what the teacher was saying. In addition, the mother was to show her son illustrations about archery to help him become one-pointed and more focused. When he was at home trying to recall what his teacher had said, all he had to do was to breathe out three times and he would remember. And he did!

Despite a congenital heart defect, which a doctor had predicted would kill her at a young age, Colette lived an active, joyful life teaching, healing, and sharing her wisdom until her last day on earth. She left both a legacy of students trained in her method in Israel and abroad, and her own writings of teaching tales, poetry, and imagery exercises. Her students have carried on the work, each with their own fingerprint — through clinical practice, teaching, writing, film, and other artistic endeavors.

In October of 1995, Colette received the award of "*Yekirat Yerushalayim*"(Beloved of Jerusalem), a richly deserved tribute to her selfless devotion. Although Colette left this earthly plane in November 2003 at the age of 94, her life's mission and teaching live on. As the sages taught:[42]

Of these, you will enjoy the fruits in this very life, and they will remain as abiding riches in the life to come.

Epilogue
Ascent of a Soul

On the first day of the Jewish month of *Kislev,* the month of Cha-
nukah, I came to what was to be my last meeting with Colette.

On greeting her, I asked: "How are you feeling?"

Not answering the question, she said, with a sparkle in her
eyes: "You finally did it! You have been able to transmit my teaching…" she then added, "but you removed my work on the ascent
of the soul! This is the only thing I borrowed from the mystics of
Safed, and it is very important."

"Colette, it was precisely those exercises that gave me the
desire to write about your work. But you forbade me to publish
them!" I exclaimed.

I recalled the first soirée I had ever attended in her house on
the eve of *Shavuot* holiday. Colette explained that she had prepared the soul ascent exercises to complete the preparation and
cleansing for the festival. "Their effects are twofold," she told us.
"First of all, they cleanse the guilt that every person, having lost a
loved one, feels for not having done enough to help the departed
soul. Secondly, it is a personal experience in which you imagine
yourself reaching the heavenly realm. The feelings and emotions
you return with enrich your conscious awareness of the higher
self, the part of you directly connected to the Source of all Life,
and empower you to succeed in your life mission."

When I showed Colette the first version of the manuscript,
she insisted that these exercises must be removed. Visualizing the
soul's ascent can be such a deep experience that it could be danger-

ous to a reader to do it without another person present to assist the imager, if needed, to return down to our everyday earthly reality. However, nearing the end of her life, she did not want these precious gifts to remain unpublished and lost to the world.

"I will add the exercises," I said to her. "I am so glad, Colette, so glad! But tell me, how are you feeling?"

"I have an edema in my lungs," she said quietly. "That means that my brain may be affected..." Colette had always counseled others not to make a tragedy of the drama of their lives. Even near death, she maintained her faith and equilibrium.

"Colette," I said to her, "The Holy One will be loving: I know it..."

She smiled at me. "Go now. Let me keep your manuscript a few days longer so that I can finish it. You can come Friday at one."

And loving He was. A few hours later, Colette gave Him back her soul in a gentle breath, in her own final ascent.

Colette's Last Message

The night following Colette's burial, I opened the manuscript and found an inserted page with her handwriting. Somehow, when Colette had read the section, *Reconnecting to Our Higher Self*, she found the strength to make notes of the main verses and notate other related psalms. The following is a replica of Colette's notations and underlinings, an invaluable memento of her understanding of illness. The Hebrew word "hafachta," to reverse, encompasses Colette's life's work. She taught everyone to reverse their life's circumstances, to put themselves in God's hand, and to reconnect to the divine through the use of mental imagery and imagination. She brought a singular joy, or in Hebrew, "simcha," to all who came in touch with her.

King David
You have <u>reversed</u> (hafachta) <u>all his inner</u>
<u>harmony</u> during his sickness.

There was not a word of my tongue *yet you God*
already knew it <u>all</u>.
See that He will plunge <u>pain and sores</u> in the <u>depths</u> of the sea.
Imagine that you say: <u>You open your hand</u>
and satisfy <u>all</u> life-desires.

The 3 things we have to do when being in <u>Jerusalem</u>:
A standing kneeling
A silent cry
An immobile dance
– <u>Rav Kotzk</u>

After reading Colette's notations, Psalm 30:12 reverberated within me:
You have reversed (hafachta) my funeral eulogy (mispedi)
into a dancing (lemachol) for me.
You have opened my sack cloth
and girded me with joy (simcha).

May this Psalm be true; may the Holy One keep Colette's soul in the Light of Life and may her prayers for us be lovingly accepted on High.

—Simcha Benyosef, Jerusalem, 2016/5776

Postscript
by Dr. Catherine Shainberg

On the morning of November 25, 2003, the day that Colette died, she was in good spirits. She had just finished Simcha Benyosef's book on *Cancer Healing* and was pleased and excited. "It's the best thing Simcha has written. It's excellent," she told me. Simcha had visited her earlier that morning, before I came; and Colette had let Simcha know how happy she was with the book. She felt it was a faithful illustration of her teachings on healing and on cancer in particular.

New York, Dec. 2005

Appendix A
Reconnecting to Our Higher Self

In my own journey, I discovered that when we are ill, we each may seek to mend our connection with the Source of all Life, both within and without. As Colette taught, we have a lower self—which is animating our body, whose knowledge is limited by our present state of consciousness — and a higher self, who has access to the Source of Life. If you imagine a mantle enclosing your entire being from above to below, illness would imply one or several rips in the mantle which require repair. In reversing illness, you call on your higher self to reach out to the healing forces from Above to locate the rips and repair them, thus restoring your entire being back to wholesomeness and reinstating your connection to your Source of Life.

With the help of the exercises that follow, you can soar up to your Source of Life and mend the rips in your mantle by trusting that all you have — the good as well as the difficult — was given to you by the Source of all Life — in love — in order to help you grow into a new empowered being, able to shed all that prevents you from absorbing the healing forces from Above.

My journey has led me to understand that the healing process is God's gift to humanity. Through this process, you can reverse your life, put yourself in His hand, cast your burden on Him, and open yourself to His healing energy. As Colette said: "We come to the world with the natural ability to reach the inner dimension, the space in which the person knows: This is where I want to go and will not be deterred." When you choose healing, all your undertakings will align with your intention to repair and heal your entire being.

These exercises can be used *at any time during the 12-phase program*. Each of us has our own unique timetable for reconnecting to the Source of Life. If you have a strong spiritual or religious perspective, you may prefer to *precede* the 12-phase program with this group of exercises. Alternatively, you are free to do them at any point in your healing process.

Exercises of Reconnection

The following five exercises help us remember our connection to the Source of Life. In remembering this connection, we are *re-membering* ourselves as well, restoring ourselves to order and wholeness. Do these exercises sequentially or **select those that resonate with you.** Remember, the benefit comes from practicing the exercises, not merely reading them.

TREE OF LIFE
Frequency: Once per day, in the morning, for seven days.
Intention: To reconnect to your original self.

Close your eyes.

Breathe out three times.

Feel and sense your spiritual body rising like a giant luminous being up to your higher self — the part of you that is directly attached to the Source of all Life.

Breathe out.

See that your reconnection acts as a catalyst to allow yourself to be loved and energized by the rays of your higher self.

Breathe out.

Feel and see that the reconnection rejuvenates your voice and your mouth, giving to your voice the right sonority and rhythm.

Breathe out.

With every decision you make, feel and see the part of you connected to the Source of all Life, giving you the insight necessary for the quick elaboration and success of your project.

Breathe out.

Have the awareness that the Source of all Life knows everything perfectly. Connecting yourself to this Source enables you to succeed in your mission.

Breathe out.

Be aware that knowledge and power are given to you when you open yourself to the rays of your higher self that work with the Source of all Life.

Breathe out.

Have the certainty that if you lose your connection with your higher self, you can act to regain it.

Breathe out once and open your eyes.

The next exercise helps us become free of our burdens and activate our inner healing potential. We must first assert our connection with our higher self who has access to our Source of life and can direct us in our healing. All we have to do to make this connection a reality is to cast our burden in the hand of the Higher Power who is the Source of Life.

When confronted with the challenge of cancer — or any serious illness — we start by letting go of our fears and feelings of despair and devastation. As King David eloquently writes in the Book of Psalms, 55:23: "Cast your burden on God and He will sustain you." By ridding ourselves of burdens, we activate our inner healing potential. The next exercise helps us become free of our burdens.

UPLIFTING THE BURDEN

Frequency: Once per day, in the morning, for seven days.
Intention: To cast your burden on God.

Close your eyes.

Breathe out.

Imagine that the Source of Life is diminishing the burden that is crushing you.

Breathe out.

See that "He will plunge pain and sores into the depths of the sea," where they are purified and disappear.

Breathe out.

He will plunge all errors, faults, guilts, into the depths of the sea.

Breathe out.

Find yourself in God's Hand.

Breathe out and open your eyes.

The following exercise reinforces your new awareness and infuses you with inner joy.

LIFE DESIRE

Frequency: Once per day, in the morning, for seven days.
Intention: To open your life channels and be surrounded with Divine light.

Close your eyes.

Breathe out three times.

Having your intention in mind, see yourself in Jerusalem on Mt. Zion's Temple Mount and breathe out.

Say together with King David: "You open Your hand and satisfy all life's desire."

Breathe out one time and open your eyes.

The following is one of Colette's most beautiful healing exercises.

Ascent to Health

Frequency: Once per day, in the morning, for seven days.

Intention: To heal.

Close your eyes.

Breathe out three times slowly.

Have an intention-direction.

Look at an ascending staircase.

Breathe out.

Keeping in mind your intention, climb up the staircase, seeing some of the disease, defects, or difficulties falling away every ten steps.

Breathe out.

When you reach the top of the staircase, you [imaginally] proclaim loudly your intention.

Breathe out.

Hear your own voice saying and singing:

"You open Your hand and scrub out the **dis-** of **dis**ease."

Breathe out.

See the hand of God satisfying your desire to be cleansed of everything that has to be swept away.

Breathe out.

Feel and know the Divine luminous energy as a transparent, enlivening shower of light. See it and sense it totally.

Breathe out one time and open your eyes.

RECONNECTION

Frequency: Once a day in the morning, for seven days.

Intention: To reconnect to your Source of Life.

Close your eyes.

Breathe out.

Into the double mirror see yourself fragmented, far from the Source. Imaginally, with your left hand, clean out the mirror from right to left. Now turn the mirror over and see yourself reconnected to the Source by any or all of the following:

- o By informing yourself
- o By conforming yourself
- o By reforming yourself
- o By transforming yourself.

Breathe out one time and open your eyes.

Appendix B
Reversing Distressing Emotions and Trauma

Sometimes in the course of doing imagery, you experience a disturbing or distressing emotion or image. Here is a simple pail-of-water-and-brush reversing technique that enables you to rid yourself of such emotions or images. Actually, this handy imagery technique can be applied any time — during the day, while practicing your daily imagery, in nighttime reversing, or to correct a distressing dream.

PAIL & WATER EXERCISE

With eyes open or closed, breathe out one time.

Identify the emotion, feeling or thought you want to neutralize or change. Is it guilt, frustration, fear, anxiety, etc.? See, sense and feel it for a moment.

Cleanse the experience or feeling, in the screen of your mind, with a golden pail of pure water and a golden brush.

If you find that the unwanted emotion is more entrenched in you or recurs often, continue the exercise as follows with eyes closed:

Go back in time, looking for another incident in which you have experienced the same feeling or emotion toward a person. Cleanse the experience or feeling, in the screen of your mind, with a golden pail of pure water and a golden brush.

If it's a repetitive situation, you may stop at every two or five years until you reach the earliest childhood incident that you can recall. Alternatively, you may find one incident that encapsulates them all and reverse it.

Every time you experience the emotion along the way, cleanse the scene of the difficulty, the time and place in which it happened, the circumstances, and the people involved with the golden pail of water and the golden brush.

Now come forward in time to the present, and pay attention to the changes provoked by this change of the past. See and feel how it is improved without that harmful emotion.

Finally, see yourself three years from now and five years from now, engaged in the mission you came here to do, having left the disease behind.

Here is a variation to remove painful or traumatic experiences.

Seeing Tomorrow [43]

Frequency: Each morning, for 21 days, or fewer if the difficulty is resolved before then. Do the exercise for up to one minute each time.

Intention: To get rid of a painful feeling or situation.

Close your eyes.

Breathe out three times.

Imagine yourself now in the situation you are experiencing as painful.

Then see how you look at this situation one week from today; then one month from today; then one year from today.

At each instance, know that the current situation is in the past. Note what you sense and feel.

Now breathe out, and open your eyes.

As you peel away the layers of unwanted emotions, you may find that you are more able to experience the past traumatic events of your life without the judgmental attitude that was injurious to your mind and body. Likewise, you may notice that you are less reactive to everyday events that have been sapping your energy and your intention to heal.

For Women Only: Addressing a Past Abortion

While doing this program, a number of women in my clinical practice have reported having an image or memory of an abortion that they had undergone in their younger years. On sharing the image, some have expressed deep emotions such as sadness, regret, or guilt. I encouraged each to repair the image. I also suggested they make a repair in the outer world in any manner that aligned with their beliefs and orientations. For some of my clients, the repair of this particular memory/event stimulated an immense improvement in their condition and even remission.

If the recollection of an earlier abortion applies to you, you may correct the image/memory as follows:

Close your eyes.

Breathe out three times slowly.

See yourself taking a pail of water and a brush and washing away the image to the left.

Then, if you wish, you may see yourself ascending a ladder.

At the top, see yourself expressing regret — or any other emotion connected to the event — to the One in whose hand is the Source of Life.

If you wish, see yourself making a contribution to charity.

Breathe out one time and, reversing your steps, descend back the way you came knowing that all has been set aright.

Breathe out once and open your eyes.

If you committed yourself to giving to charity, either through a financial donation or volunteer work, follow through with the act as soon as you are able. The advantage is that your entire being is involved in the repair. For religious individuals, see footnote.[44]

Appendix C
Nighttime Reversing

Nighttime Reversing is a short imagery exercise performed just before you go to bed. In it, you correct the typical repetitive, distressing emotions and conflictual social interactions of the day.

The exercise not only clears your mind and helps you to fall asleep easily, but heightens your awareness and assists you in overcoming chronic reactions and behaviors that weigh you down.

Colette considered it a pivotal daily practice for personal development, spiritual growth, and healing in general. Here is her full version of the exercise.

While you are lying in bed with your eyes closed, breathe out once and see yourself go over your day in reverse order, event by event.

Start with the last event of the day and relive it in imagery, correcting your behavior as needed.

Go to the next-to-last event and relive it, changing whatever needed correcting.

Continue in reverse order until you reach the time when you woke up.

Recall each event, correcting your attitude and behavior in those situations where you had difficulty.

Try to obtain something that you wanted for yourself that day but couldn't get.

If you had a troubling conversation with someone, recall the conversation as close to verbatim as possible, but imagine the other person's words coming out in your voice and your words coming out in his or her voice. In adopting the dialogue of the other, you will come to understand his/her experience.[45] (In waking life, you may call that person the next day to make amends if you wish).

Finish the exercise by seeing, sensing, and feeling yourself awaking to the morrow, your entire being radiant with gratitude for the gift of life.

You may find that you fall asleep without completing the entire exercise — that's fine. It is the consistency of the practice that bears fruit. Nighttime Reversing takes mental energy, so if you find yourself too fatigued to do the entire exercise, you may streamline the exercise and correct only the most disturbing event(s) of the day or skip it entirely and stay focused on the core program exercises. Shorthand variations follow the set of examples below.

EXAMPLES OF NIGHTTIME REVERSING

Let's say you're rushing to prepare an elegant dinner for company at eight. As you go through the afternoon, you make an effort to control the rising tension. At seven, however, a small incident makes you explode. The dinner then goes on as scheduled.

Before bed, you do a Nightime Reversing exercise. With eyes closed, breathing out one long exhalation through your mouth, you review your day on the screen of your mind, working backwards from the last event of the night to the first event of the morning. Going back over the day's events in reverse order, you relive the incident that made you angry, and you see that it is the anxiety you felt over your expected guests that caused the anger.

You see yourself anxiously eyeing the clock, wondering if the soufflé you have in the oven will hold its own until the guests arrive. You then see your children fighting over some candy they have snatched from the decorations of the dinner table. Instead of visualizing your violent anger fit, you correct the event by seeing yourself going over to the children and asking them to cooperate. You see yourself giving them a bag containing healthy snacks. You later congratulate them for keeping so quiet.

You have reversed the event by visualizing yourself mastering the incident. You now have the guidelines to reproduce this new mode of behavior at will. By going back to the way you felt before your anxiety came about and observing what could have been a more appropriate reaction, you receive an additional supply of energy that can help you avoid anxiety in the future.

Here's an example from my practice: The mother of an unruly youth complained about the anger that always disturbed her relationship with her grown son. A week of nighttime reversing enabled her to see that it was always in the morning, when he was barely awake after a night of partying, that she piled her various complaints on him.

"You left the room a mess; your cigarette-ashes are all over the place; you never wash your dishes; you used my car without asking me and left me without gas," etc. From her point of view, it was perfectly logical to tell him what she felt when she first saw him because it might be the only time she saw him all day.

Reversing the incidents, she looked at it taking his role. She saw herself with her mind clouded by the abuse of the night before, simply unable to react to the assault of complaints in any other way than by screaming, "Leave me alone!" She decided to arrange an hour that was mutually convenient in the late afternoon for them to spend some time together, and in the middle of a pleasant exchange she presented her complaints.

Since he no longer felt attacked, he was able to reply sensibly and even made some changes to please her. The relationship changed completely, to the point that he sought out a mentor, who helped him grow and mature.

Here's another example of Nighttime Reversing: A young man worked during the day and attended night school. He complained of stomach pains and fatigue that resulted in inefficiency. In his nightly reversing exercise, he first saw himself before going to bed, attempting to work on a paper but feeling sluggish and unable to concentrate. He then saw himself a moment earlier in time eating cookies, and finally, earlier still, energetically setting up his papers and snack in order to start working.

Nighttime Reversing allowed him to see the pattern of behavior that was at the source of his complaints. Whenever he had a paper to write, he wouldn't spend time to get a proper meal and instead piled coffee and cookies on his desk. It took a few nights of reversing to realize that it was the sugar intake that his body was reacting against.

Reading thousands of pages on the negative effects of sugar would not have had the effect of actually seeing in his mind's eye the energy he felt before ingesting it. He then visualized himself working enthusiastically on some project, with different healthy snacks around his papers.

Seeing himself with the corrected behavior actually gave him the energy to change. Subsequently, by taking the time to eat nutritious meals he found that at the end of a working day he had a lot of energy for his schoolwork.

Before the nightly self-evaluation, he had assumed that he was naturally tired after a full day's work. He was unable to see what was happening to him because his motives were good: He did not want to waste precious time looking for ways to feed his body at the expense of his intellect! In the reversing exercise he experienced the energy he felt prior to eating cookies. He was then able to relate the lack of strength to the food and to realize that caring for his body would give him additional energy to succeed in all his undertakings.

Although altering our reactions to emotional stress appears daunting we can enlist the aid of our mind's eye to change. Very often a certain emotion or pattern of events causes you to exhibit a trait that you would like to alter. Reversing identifies the emotion and cleanses it. This breaks the pattern: the memory of your behavior stays with you, but you are no longer linked to it. You are no longer prisoner of the emotion, the pattern of events, or of the effect an event has had on you.

Another example: A young man was suffering from a deep depression. He complained of being unable to feel; he related to everyone around him with complete apathy. After using the reversing exercise regularly for about six months, he saw in his mind's eye that his problem originated in his childhood. His mother was often prey to fits of rage that she was unable to control. The boy would then become very sad, for he felt that he was deprived of motherly love.

As he grew, he learned to avoid painful emotional insights by intellectualizing his life; he blocked all feelings. The nightly introspection eventually helped him to identify his feeling of sadness, and to realize that just as he had been able to feel sad, he could also feel happy. From that moment, the memory of his childhood no longer triggered apathy in him, and he became cured of his depression.

A person can hear hours of lectures on how to behave, but it will be difficult to use that information to grow because s/he cannot see him/herself objectively. Most people usually display an astonishing sensitivity to critical remarks. This is not only the case if the criticisms suggested are off base, but even more so if they are accurate.

The advantage of nighttime reversing is that you are not just hearing someone tell you what you are doing wrong — you are seeing it from the other person's perspective. It is as if you witnessed your son/daughter acting less than perfectly: Your built-in response is a desire to improve his/her behavior. This desire, now applied to yourself, is the best incentive to correct what you observed.

Here is one more example from my practice of how to imaginally reverse a behavior through the use of Nighttime Reversing.

Lenora was told by her oncologist to avoid alcohol and wheat in her diet. Lenora would stick to her diet all week long, but once a week she had a special dinner with her husband in which she rewarded herself for her efforts. The problem is that in this dinner, she would drink heavily as well as indulge in white bread. The next day, she would feel physically unwell and guilty.

Upon learning about the Nightly Reversing exercise, she returned to the scene of the special dinner. To correct the over-indulgence, she sees herself drinking one glass of wine with delight at the very beginning of the meal. By the second course, her husband surprises her by bringing her a special drink he has created for her out of jasmine green tea with ginger and a natural sweetener. She sees herself enjoying the treat so much that she is able to abstain from wine for the rest of the meal.

She then visualized her daughter bringing her a home-baked spelt roll. Lenora finds herself so moved that she is satisfied with half a roll. I instructed Lenora to repeat this short exercise each day in the morning for seven days. In the weeks that followed, Lenora reported that she was able to adhere to her diet as well as other medical advice she had previously ignored.

SHORTER VARIATIONS ON NIGHTTIME REVERSING EXERCISE

As noted above, Nighttime Reversing takes mental energy, so here are some short variations to play with. Choose one or more of the following approaches to nighttime reversing, depending on your energy levels and your focus. In all cases, you are imprinting a new way of being when confronted with difficult circumstances.

1. Reverse or correct any disagreeable episodes you experienced during the day. Correct them in any way you desire. For example, see the corrected scene. Alternatively, you might use the Golden Pail and Brush Exercise to cleanse the memory of the event as follows: Cleanse the experience or feeling imaginally with a golden pail of clear water and a golden brush — cleansing the scene of the difficulty, the time and place in which it happened, the circumstances, and the people involved.

2. Reverse a conflictual situation by becoming the other person and experiencing it from his or her perspective, and then correcting your own behavior.

3. Choose a specific trait you wish to change for 21 days. For example, if you are easily angered, review your day in reverse order correcting any incident in which you became angered.

Finish any variation of the exercise by planting a new vision of tomorrow: See, sense, and feel yourself awaking to the morrow; your entire being radiant with gratitude for the gift of life.

Appendix D
For Clinicians

Although this is a book for a lay audience, I have included several imagery exercises for use by clinicians trained in imagery. These include:

1) Opening Exercises for a New Client

2) Repairing Relationships:

    - With a spouse or significant other

    - With the departed (Ascent Exercises)

Initiating Treatment

INTRODUCTORY EXERCISES

Prior to meeting with a new patient, I pray for Divine guidance. I ask to be a messenger of the Divine Healer to help this sufferer enter the healing phase. I visualize myself within a circle.[46] I quietly ask God for compassion for this patient as I imagine white healing light coming down from Above and infusing the patient. I continue to say this short prayer before each meeting.

Next, I select several exercises for the session that I later find to have providentially fit the needs of the patient. I refer here not only to the patient's need to heal but also to the life circumstances facing the patient at that moment.

I generally begin the session with a **cleansing** exercise (see Phases 5 and 6 in Chapter III), followed by either the **Arrows** or **Castle** exercise provided below; both these diagnostic exercises help to uncover the source of the blockages that are reflected in the physical illness. Thereafter, I continue with the **Ring of Keys** exercise in the first or second session.

I have included two examples from my practice using the **Arrows** and **Castle** exercises. I strongly encourage patients to allow their own images to come through within the guided images they are seeing. These personal images are the ones that the patient takes "as homework," as they stem directly from the patient's higher self. In my examples below, note how I weave in a cleansing exercise using a pail and water (i.e. retracing and correcting of the past exercise)" when the patient encounters a long-standing blockage, habit, attitude, or emotion. This reverse journey allows the patient to see clearly, unclouded by the habitual mind. This insertion of a "mini" retracing of the past exercise is my own particular style that I have found useful, but of course the exercises can be done as they are written.

EXERCISES TO DISCOVER THE SOURCE(S) OF THE BLOCKAGE

Arrows

Close your eyes.

Breathe out three times.

Stand in a meadow. At your waist, you have a bag with golden arrows.

Align your right arm and your right leg to your right. Your finger holding the bow faces right as well.

Now close your eyes and shoot an arrow to your right as far as you can. Now to your left. Observe where the arrows land. Now close your eyes and shoot an arrow directly in front of you. Observe where the arrow lands.

Then turn to face behind you and, after closing your eyes, shoot an arrow in that direction: Observe where the arrow lands.

Now retrieve the arrows.

What do you discover when you retrieve the arrows?

Breathe out and open your eyes.

CASTLE

Close your eyes.

Breathe out three times.

See yourself dressed in a white suit of armor and riding a white horse.

Breathe out one time.

Know your mission and conquer a castle single-handedly.

When you succeed, breathe out one time.

Find your way to the dungeon — the room where one is forgotten. Here, prisoners were thrown down and abandoned until they died.

Go downstairs carefully and see whether there is anyone there who is still alive. Start a conversation with the prisoner, and find out who s/he is and what message s/he has for you about healing your malady or disease. Decide whether you are going to let the prisoner go and act upon your decision.

Breathe out one time.

Let the castle staff provide for the needs of the prisoner and come back upstairs to the light of day.

Go around the castle till you reach the main gate.

Now enter the castle through its main gate as the new rightful lord.

The first thing you must do is find the hidden room in which the castle lord keeps the prisoners who are too important to be eliminated.

Go and see who is there and free him or her after the forgotten one gives you a message about your malady or disease.

Breathe out once.

Know that every lord of a castle keeps a "Book of Reason" where he records daily notes of what is important for posterity. See the book and read what is written for yesterday. Inscribe something for today. See the inscription that will be there to-morrow.

RING OF KEYS

Close your eyes.

Breathe out three times.

Find yourself in front of the Gate of Healing, a gate with many locks. In your hand is a ring of keys. Study the keys for a moment. Quickly, choose the key to open the lock that opens the Gate.

What do you discover?

Keep whatever you discover for yourself.

Breathe out and open your eyes.

Do this exercise once if the client succeeds in opening the **Gate of Healing**. If the client is unable to open the Gate, remind the client that anything can happen in imagination and ask the client to bring whatever is necessary to open the Gate. If the client is still unable to open the gate, move on to the cleansing exercises at the beginning of Chapter III, "The Core Program." You may have the client try the **Ring of Keys** exercise again in a few weeks. You can, of course, expand on this exercise as an entry point for a deeper exploration.

I once gave the **Ring of Keys** exercise to a young woman who experienced mild difficulties to open the gate. She tried several keys in the ring but some were too large and others too small and they did not work on the gate. Suddenly noticing a small key that seemed to be the right size; she tried it and the gate opened right away. She went inside and found a beautiful garden.

Example #1: John

At 72 years old, John had prostate cancer. Upon doing the Castle exercise, he eliminated the enemies surrounding the castle in no time. In the underground prison, he found a man who was a political prisoner. When John conversed with him, the man informed him that the government did not want him around because he spoke the truth. As the leader of the resistance movement, the army now sought to eliminate him.

John then came up and entered the castle though its main gate. He went up the stairs and located the hidden room. In it, he found a very wise older man who was the mastermind of the resistance movement. He was fighting for justice and was very strong and very wise.

I asked John what specific feelings or emotions did the conversation with the underground prisoner arouse in him. "I feel righteous within," he said. When I told him to explain himself further, he added: "I have the thought 'I am righteous' going through my head." I then asked John to go back in time, stopping at every five years, to see when he had experienced a similar feeling of righteousness, in totally different circumstances.

"I see myself talking with my last wife," said John after a moment of imaging. "I am telling her off, because she has done the wrong thing. I don't remember what she did, but I am re-experiencing the feeling I had then, that I was the one who was right in our discussion."

I asked him to go further back in time, and to keep looking for that same feeling of being right:

I see myself in an argument with my daughter Marcia, who was then seventeen. Marcia had just been kicked out of school for disappearing for two days while I was away on a business trip. I kept pressing her to tell me where she had gone. She finally divulged that she had been helping an impoverished woman and her six small children to relocate after she received an eviction notice for defaulting on her rent. When I asked her why she had not explained this to her principal, Marcia said that all kindness has to be done in secret. I screamed at her for her stupidity, for possibly jeopardizing her future, and for not understanding that kindness begins at home.

I then asked John to use a pail of crystal clear water and a golden brush and imaginally cleanse the scenes of any difficult exchanges, the time and place in which they happened, the circumstances, and the people involved. John then had to come forward in time and pay attention to the changes provoked by his change of the past. I asked him to tell me any changes he saw in the present after correcting these scenes of the past.

"I see myself with my wife," he said. "I am still married to her." A tear rolled down the old man's cheek as he spoke these words. "My daughter is married, but I see her still in communication with me. She plans to visit me this coming weekend."

John's visualization of the man in the underground prison helped him experience his own resistant, judgmental nature through the course of his life. Often, he assumed that other people had malicious intent. He had gone through four successive marriages and had later divorced under the assumption that his different wives were selfish in their expectations of him.

John had never tried to view the situation from their perspective; he now found himself alone and miserable, as he was unable to be in an intimate relationship. Through the exercise, he was able to deal with others more maturely, understanding that external pressures pushed a person to act in certain way, and that it was unfair to assume that the other person was either all good or all bad.

"It is too late for marriage," he added, somewhat bitterly, "but I am going to apply what I have learned in my relationship with my children."

John's children later reported how their father had grown from the experience of his illness and how much easier it was to relate to him and to love him rather than just being forced to respect him.

Example #2: Pauline

Pauline visited me with the hope of correcting uncontrollable food bingeing that she has suffered from since adolescence. Pauline gains a lot of weight, then goes on a strict diet and loses the weight, only to start the process anew. She joined Overeaters Anonymous for several years and has been through different "abstinences" i.e., eliminating one or more items from her daily diet. She is able to respect the intended time of abstinence, but her problem remains. Pauline feels very distressed by her "abnormality." I asked her to imaginally conquer a castle single-handedly, and she succeeded. She first went to the underground prison, and when she pointed her lantern into the darkened cell, she found a psychologically disturbed male.

"What do you feel before this man?" I asked her.

"I feel nurturing love and responsibility," she said.

"Now go back in time, stopping at every five years, searching for when you experienced a similar feeling in what may be totally different circumstances."

After a moment's silence, Pauline said, "I see my parents at different times in our lives. The words 'nurturing love and responsibility' lead me back to my parents."

I suggested that she should have the castle servants take care of the prisoner's needs and send him off to freedom, but she said that he was a good man and she did not necessarily want to send him off.

Pauline then entered the castle through the main gate and followed my instructions trying to find the hidden prison in which the important prisoners were kept. In this concealed room, Pauline found eyes looking at her. She was not sure to whom they belonged.

"Why have you been imprisoned?" asked Pauline.

The eyes laughed and told Pauline, "You know why I am here."

Pauline claimed that she did not know. I had her ask the eyes again, and the answer she received was: "I was caught for lying."

"What do you feel at this reply?" I asked her.

"I feel shame," she answered softly.

I asked Pauline to go back in time once again, looking for the first time in which she had experienced an encounter with "lying and shame."

Pauline ended up in tears as she relived a scene in which she stole a diary from the desk of her Italian teacher, on whom she had a crush. She then proceeded to call many of the numbers in the book, despite the inner shame she felt at invading her teacher's privacy. She had to lie in the process, but was found out when the phone bill was received with several calls made to Italy. Then she felt intense shame, and her parents did not speak to her for a week. Pauline's attitude now showed how she was still under the influence of her ordeal and her parents' disappointment in her.

"Cleanse the experience in the screen of your mind with a golden pail of pure water and a golden brush," I instructed her. "Cleanse the scene of the difficulty, the time and place in which it happened, the circumstances, and the people involved."

Pauline complied. However, when she tried once again to identify the eyes of her hidden prisoner, she said that she could not do it.

Thus ended the first session with Pauline. In the following session, I told Pauline that I wanted her to again visit the hidden upstairs room of the castle because there were questions left unanswered.

"Tell your prisoner to wash his hands in the sink, which is in the corner of the room," I suggested. "Now, stand behind him and look at his reflection in the mirror."[47]

"I see him now!" exclaimed Pauline. "It is a boy younger than I with whom I had an intimate relation at the beginning of my puberty years, a few years before the phone book episode. We did not consummate the relationship, and his parents then moved to a different state. I was too embarrassed to talk about it to my parents, and at the same time, unable to integrate the experience."

Pauline admitted that the first time she did the exercise the image of this young man suggested itself in the upstairs prison room but she had rejected it.

I told Pauline to go back in time looking for scenes in which she saw herself lying, and stop at every five years until she reached childhood. Every time she saw herself lying, she had to cleanse the scene, the shame she felt, and all the people involved. When she reached the age of five, she had to cleanse the scene of her trauma.

I told Pauline to go back in time looking for scenes in which she saw herself experiencing the same quality of shame provoked by her image, and stop at every five years until she reached childhood. Pauline was taken back to the aftermath of the stolen phone book, when she felt a sexual arousal that she attempted to assuage by eating a treat. She made the comment that she now saw herself several times stifling a budding sexuality for which she felt she had no outlet but binge eating.

I told her to cleanse every single one of these scenes, going back in time until her encounter with the boy; she had to cleanse the scene, the shame she felt, and all the people involved. I asked her to come forward in time to the present, and see the changes provoked by this change of the past. Pauline saw an older version of herself happily married and preparing a meal for the coming Sabbath.

When we discussed her visualization, Pauline expressed a great sense of release upon understanding that the phone book incident had awaken a sexuality which had been dormant since her episode with the boy. This left her with a hunger for which she had an inability, fused with unwillingness, to identify, that she attempted to satisfy with food.

I suggested to Pauline to volunteer in a soup kitchen or any food related charity and to reserve treats for the Sabbath day. Pauline decided to abstain from wheat and sugar during the six weekdays and enrolled as an unpaid assistant every Thursday night in a charitable organization that collected all the unused meals in a large wedding hall, packed them, and delivered to the homes of poor families.

Not long after our encounter, Pauline met a young man and started a deep relationship that lead to the marriage she had visualized.

Repairing Relationships

Imaging Marital Harmony

Over the years, I have become aware that spouses, partners, and family do not always rise to the occasion of the challenge of supporting their partner, finding themselves unable to face the sudden increase in the demand for emotional and physical support they now must provide. Cancer patients often have the additional challenge of not allowing the disease to destroy their marriage, or their marital difficulties to affect the healing process. Here again, imagery is a powerful ally.

Harmony of Small Changes Exercise

One simple exercise that Colette devised to help restore harmony in a relationship is to have each spouse or partner do an imagery exercise, either together or separately, in which they see themselves entering a stage by different doors.

On the stage, imaginally, each spouse asks the other: "What would you like me to do for you?" and carefully listens to the *small* concrete change that their partner desires. After the imagery is complete, the couple opens their eyes, and each verbally asks the other what small change he or she would like. Each person is to then integrate the verbal and imaginal requests of the other into daily life.

I have witnessed a number of cases in which doing a small concrete action to please an ailing spouse helps the healthy spouse provide the unconditional love and support required at that crucial time in the fight against disease. The same basic exercise can hold for other kinds of partners, for family members, and for friends.

DREAMS OF HARMONY EXERCISE

As a follow-up exercise, ask each spouse to request a dream that may help restore marital harmony, using the following technique:

Have a diary on your night table opened to a blank page with the next day's date at the top of the page, thus asserting your intention to remember your dream.

Immediately prior to falling asleep, request or pray for a dream that will help you attain marital harmony. I have found it useful to state out loud three times, before expressing the dream request at night: "Tomorrow morning I will remember to think of my dreams before moving or opening my eyes."

The next morning, remember not to open your eyes before trying to see whether you had a dream. As you remember your dream, still with your eyes closed, roll over, since it is often the case that you will remember a different scene of your dream when switching positions.

Then open your eyes and sit up to write or record your dream, for it is likely to evaporate with your morning activity if not recorded. Drawing your dream often helps. If writing is not an option, record it on a cell phone or discuss it with a member of your family, asking this person to help you remember it.

The couple then returns to the next therapy session with the dream each one of them had. If either one of them does not receive a dream upon request, s/he may use another dream they have had in the recent past. Here is an excerpt of Colette explaining the process:

Each spouse is going to dream the dream of the other, so that they become reunited within. Outside is the friction of daily life; within is togetherness. Each spouse must come to the next session with a dream that they will tell. The therapist must ask each one of them what is most important in the dream of the other spouse. You, the therapist, must then choose one image from what each one of them has stated and make a separate exercise for each of them, incorporating the other's significant dream image. Upon doing these exercises throughout the next week, both spouses will be building a mutual bond within.

Here is as an example of dream work to promote marital harmony. Sarah came to see me after an incidence of breast cancer. She found that she could not identify the main blockages in her life through either of the two diagnostic exercises given above. As Norman Cousins points out: *Cancer patients do not always recognize or identify their feelings.*[48]

Unperturbed, I asked her to pray for Divine guidance in a dream, as to what she could do to bring about a healing, and warned her that dreams do not always come upon request. Her dream – which came within two days of asking for it – showed a disconnection from her husband. When I asked her about their situation, she said that Isaac, her husband, was completely engrossed by his job and did not relate to her in the slightest. They never shared any time together. All my suggestions to improve their relationship were turned down with an apathetic "No, he is just not interested."

I told her that for the next visit, she must bring Isaac with her. Several weeks went by in which I did not hear from her. When she eventually called, she said that he was a very busy man and could not come at the hours I usually received patients. I told her that he should suggest a time which was possible for him, and I would try to free myself then.

When we finally met, I asked to see him first while she waited in a different room. I explained to him how important it was for Sarah that their relationship be harmonious. Isaac was noncommittal, but he willingly accepted to be involved in the imagery I was suggesting.

On the stage, Isaac saw Sarah asking him to sit with her for some time on Sundays and be involved in an activity together, such as studying a book on a topic they were both interested in. It took a long time for Isaac to see himself asking Sarah to do something for him, but he finally said, "When we have dinner together, she should sit with me and listen to what I have to tell her."

After the imagery section, I asked him, "Doesn't she sit with you at dinner?" He replied, "Yes, but she is not with me; I can see that her mind is on another million things. Furthermore, she gets up many times throughout the course of dinner, disrupting any conversation we may be having."

When I suggested that he help her serve dinner, he retorted, "I thought of that and we have different shifts to serve dinner. However, even when it is my turn, she will still get up when I am in the middle of telling her something that is important to me."

I then asked Isaac to wait outside and had Sarah come in. It took me the longest time to convince her to try to participate in this type of imagery exercise. She kept saying that it would not work. Upon doing the exercise, she was initially unable to see herself asking Isaac to do something for her.

"He should stop talking to his mother about me, and not be so close to her," she finally said. "The woman is ruining our lives together."

"That may be correct," I insisted, "but focus on one small concrete change, try again."

"He should sit with me a few minutes every day and tell me something that happened to him in the course of the day," she said. As for her own visualization of what he wanted from her, Sarah said, "He asks that I no longer rebuke him."

When we discussed her findings a moment later, Sarah said, "It will be very difficult for me to stop rebuking him. I do that very often. Furthermore, I am not even sure that he would want me to! He often says, 'thank you for pointing it out to me.'"

I then saw the couple together. Upon hearing that his wife had seen him asking her to stop rebuking him and that she offered to take his request upon herself in their daily lives, Isaac nodded with evident appreciation in his eyes. Before they left, I asked each one of them to elicit a dream for the second facet of the marital harmony imaging work.

In the second session, Sarah told us the following dream she had received upon request, "I see myself in a space I cannot identify together with my neighbor, who is a sweet woman. My neighbor closes her eyes, looking as if she were going to faint. I say to myself: Why should I help her? I don't have the strength!"

Since Isaac had not received a dream at his request, he told us a dream he had had not long before, "I am the chef in a dairy restaurant. I have recently expanded my repertoire to learning about the benefits of raw food. In my dream, I see myself at a reception organized by a young couple to celebrate the recovery of the wife from a serious illness. One of the desserts I prepared was a raw creation. It was a lot of work but I wanted to show both of them how raw food could be a gourmet experience and not just a way to maintain one's health. In the dream I stood there in dismay upon realizing that they had only nibbled at my beautiful handiwork."

In the discussion that followed, Sarah selected the image of a meal celebrating the wife's recovery. Isaac focused on the words of Sarah's dream, "looking as if she were going to faint."

I asked Sarah to see herself at a dinner that her husband organized to thank God for her recovery, where the entire menu consisted of raw food creations. I told her to see herself expressing her appreciation to Isaac, and to look at the pleasure he took of seeing her enjoy what he had painstakingly prepared.

I then asked Isaac to visualize his wife in a state of intense weakness, "looking as if she were going to faint." I told him to see himself telling her, "I will help you to help others and then you will be able to help yourself as well."

To the couple's credit, they both adopted these changes into their lives, and this effort improved the quality of their life together. This gave Sarah happiness in her marriage and boosted her energy to fight the disease.

ASCENT EXERCISES: REPAIRING RELATIONSHIPS WITH THE DEPARTED

In the therapeutic setting, clients often express feelings of guilt, anger, or grief regarding a deceased relative. The following two exercises are designed to repair relationships with the deceased and cleanse distressing feelings. They also allow us the possibility of union with the One. Colette considered these *ascent exercises* amongst her most beautiful and *powerful*. As such, they need to be done under the supervision of a trained guide or clinician.

Clients should choose only <u>one</u> of the two exercises:

Use **Journey of the Soul** if the client is grieving and wishes to accompany a *recently* departed relative or friend.

Use **Way to Paradise** if the client wishes to repair a relationship and erase any lingering guilt for not having done enough for the relative when he or she was alive. Do this exercise at least one month after the loved one's death, or even years later.

After completing either exercise, it is important that the client return and *descend* back into the body sensing and feeling him/herself back in the chair, feet on the floor, grounded in everyday reality.

JOURNEY OF THE SOUL

This exercise is used to accompany the soul of a recently departed relative or friend.

Close your eyes.

Breathe out three times slowly.

Create a path of white clouds.

Meet the door-keepers who are asking for the seals that are tickets for your passage.

- o   Describe them.
- o   What is engraved on your own seal? And on your parents' seal?

Sense the strong power of these pictures on the seals that are protecting you on the way.

Know that the dangers are increasing every time you reach a goal.

Sense the one hundred million waves falling on you. See their rush. Feel the impact that strikes you. Sense the cold.

Now you are surrounded by a strong fire emanating from your own body and consuming it.

- o Sense it as a danger.
- o Sense it as an ecstatic experience.
- o Sense the illumination that comes from it.
- o What are you learning from this lightning-like light in your heart?
- o Sense the purity of the world around.
- o Know in your heart that you have entered a new world and feel that "the Prince of the Presence" is not very far on the eighth firmament where the Divine Wisdom dwells.

Suddenly your path becomes a marble one and you slide on it easily until the path appears broken by a gap separating it in two.

With a clear heart, construct a bridge and describe it.

Now cross over the bridge. How do you feel? What do you see under the bridge in this abyss?

You go on your way where the marble road is again broken. What do you do?

Find a different way to have a second bridge. Describe what you do, sense, and see.

What happens when you cross the second bridge? When you reach the other side?

As you are walking on this road in the sky, you meet some beings. Who are they? Describe them. What do they say or ask for?

Now you reach a third bridge and cross it to find a third shore. What is happening? What do you see and feel?

See now the specialists who are here for the measurement of your limbs from the toenail to the top of the head.

When you have been told that you fit, see again the doorkeepers. Describe them.

Show them your second set of seals, and the others from your parents.

Now see yourself at the entrance of the higher Garden of Eden, the one in the Sky. See Angel Gabriel with his flaming sword turning around you and your departed relative (or dear friend) and receive permission to let your relative enter the garden, and there be quiet and happy forever.

Leave the Garden and return the way you came.

Breathe out once and open your eyes.

THE WAY TO PARADISE

Close your eyes.
Breathe out three times slowly.

Imagine that you see your *Ruach* [roo-ah-ch], the superior spirit, leave your body through your mouth.

Breathe out three times.

Imagine that you see your *Ruach*/spirit soaring up on its way to the original Light of Creation, the light that shines from one end of the universe to the other.

Breathe out.

Imagine, as an obstacle on the way, a wall of thorns you must break through.

Is it impassable? Can you find an exit?

You see the Garden, but between it and you there is an abyss again — an impassable abyss.

Breathe out.

Imagine that your need of the Garden is so great that the emanation of your eyes are creating a radiant bridge between it and you.

Breathe out.

You are on the other side of the bridge. How does your soul look now? Describe the River of Fire that runs on this other shore and separates you from the Garden.

Breathe out.

Dive into the fire. You have to accept this *auto da fé*, act of faith, to be totally purified of your passions.

Breathe out.

You are now in front of the Garden. Archangel Gabriel is above the door. Ask him for permission to enter and answer the three questions he is asking you.

Breathe out.

You have answered the questions. What is happening to you? To the door?

Breathe out, and look at the Garden.

Look for the *Neshama* [Neh-sha-ma], the higher soul, of the one you have loved and not forgotten. Join this soul or the soul of an ancestor and tell it of your love in your own way.

Breathe out and leave him or her or them because we have no right to stay any longer.

Breathe out.

Slowly go out of the Garden and thank Archangel Gabriel. Now, look at the River of Fire.

At this point, the clinician asks the client, "Do you want to return now to your place on the Earth? Or do you want to visit the Higher paradise? Raise your hand if you want to go on."

If the client does not wish to continue, instruct the client to imaginally return to the chair, sensing their feet flat on the ground, and their backs straight against the chair. If the client wishes to continue, instruct the client to:

Breathe out and jump up near Archangel Gabriel, asking him to show you the way to the second garden.

Breathe out. Follow his direction. Enter the garden, visit it, and absorb the understanding, knowledge, and wisdom that are given to you.

Breathe out. Return to the gate and leave with gratitude but no regrets.

Breathe out. Fly all the way to the first garden. From the top, look down at it and at the soul or souls to which you are still connected.

Breathe out. Give thanks again to Angel Gabriel and fly above the River of Fire. From afar, sense its high flames.

Breathe out and soar above the deep abyss and the bridge of light.

Breathe out and see your *Ruach*/spirit surmounting the wall of thorns, and sense only the fragrance of the roses.

Breathe out and return here. Know, sense, and feel your *Ruach*/spirit entering your mouth and joining your other souls — your *Neshama*/higher soul, and your *Nefesh* [Neh-fesh] or animal soul.

Feel the happiness of this meeting.

Sense the wholeness and unity.

Breathe out once and open your eyes.

Endnotes

[1] Gerald Epstein, *Healing Visualizations: Creating Health through Imagery*, (New York: Bantam, 1989). See also, Gerald Epstein, *Healing Into Immortality: A New Spiritual Medicine of Healing Stories and Imagery*, (New York: ACMI Press, 1997).

[2] Catherine Shainberg, *Kabbalah and the Power of Dreaming: Awakening the Visionary Life*, (Vermont: Inner Traditions, 2005).

[3] Gerald Epstein and Barbarah Fedoroff, eds. *The Encyclopedia of Mental Imagery: Colette Aboulker-Muscat's 2,100 Visualization Exercises for Personal Development, Healing, and Self-Knowledge*, (New York: ACMI Press, 2012).

[4] While this book gestated, I published four books on other facets of these observations. My first book, *Living Kabbalah: A Guide to the Sabbath and Festivals in the Teachings of Rabbi Rafael Moshe Luria*, 2nd ed. (Jerusalem: Feldheim Publishers, 2006), offers a glimpse into the state of consciousness of passionate attachment to the Divine. The second, my translation of *The Gate of Love* from the 16th century mystical manual *The Beginning of Wisdom* (Jersey City: Ktav Publishers, 2001), describes the self-preparation required for the acquisition of this higher consciousness. The third, *The Light of Ephraim: The Ascent from Temptation to Divine Consciousness*, 3rd ed., revised (Jerusalem: Koren Publishers, 2017), is about the spiritual prison in which man inadvertently encloses himself. Finally, my books, *Achoti Kalla-My Sister My Bride: Learning to Enhance the Shabbat Experience*, (New York: Moznaim Publishers, 2017)

and *I Need a Soul Companion! A Novel on the Shabbat Mystery*, (New York: Moznaim Publishers, 2017) bring to life the spiritual preparations we undertake to receive the light of holiness on the Sabbath.

[5] Simcha Benyosef, *Empowered to Heal: Therapeutic Visualizations Drawn for the Lunar Months*, (Jerusalem: Devora Publishing, 2008).

[6] Elizabeth Kübler-Ross and David Kessler, *Life Lessons*, (New York: Scribner, 2000) 222.

[7] Deepak Chopra, *Quantum Healing: Exploring the Frontiers of Mind/ Body Medicine,* (New York: Bantam Books, 1989) 15.

[8] For more information on dreams visit my website at http://www.healingwithinwithout.com or Dr. Epstein's at http://www.drjerryepstein.org

[9] Gerald Epstein, *Healing into Immortality,* 170.

[10] There are rare specific cases in which extreme caution must be applied in using imagery exercises or must be avoided altogether. For example, a person suffering from psychosis, namely, schizophrenia.

[11] Gerald Epstein, *Waking Dream Therapy: Unlocking the Secrets of Self through Dreams and Imagination* (New York: ACMI Press, 1999) 157-58.

[12] For Colette's teachings on how to elicit dreams to complete the work we do with imagery see "Instructions for Imaging" in my book *Empowered to Heal* or the "Dreams and Visualizations" page on my website. Dream corrections are best done with a trained imagery practitioner.

[13] For additional cleansing exercises, see Epstein, *Healing into Immortality*, 91–93.

[14] Epstein, *Healing Into Immortality*, 196–97.

[15] Itzhak Bentov, *Stalking the Wild Pendulum,* (New York: E. P. Dutton, 1977).

[16] This is a Lurianic kabbalistic idea, which I have often verified in my practice.

[17] Drawn from *The Bahir*, trans. Rabbi Aryeh Kaplan (New York: Samuel Weiser, 1979).

[18] I am grateful to Tehilla Chiche for seeing this solution in her imaging and sharing it with me.

[19] Drawn from the Baal Shem Tov, the founder of Hasidism.

[20] The image of "the wings of the winds" is paraphrased from Psalm 104:3.

[21] Colette created this exercise for a relative of mine, herein named Daisy, to help Daisy rid herself of a hatred she held against a younger cousin. Daisy had fed her resentment to the point that she had forbidden her children to include this cousin in any family meetings and parties. Daisy's children had agreed to this out of respect for their mother. When Daisy died all her children continued to exclude this cousin from family gatherings out of respect for their mother's memory. About two years after Daisy's death, Clara—her daughter—dreamt that her mother said to her: Make peace with your cousin. Clara fulfilled her mother's request. May this exercise and its story serve to elevate Daisy's soul and help all those clinging to past grudges release them to the Source on High and replace them with well-being.

[22] Paraphrasing the *Song of Songs* 2:4.

[23] http://en.wikipedia.org/wiki/Synagogue_of_El_Transito

[24] http://en.wikipedia.org/wiki/Synagogue_of_El_Transito

[25] Drawn from *The Bahir,* trans. Rabbi Aryeh Kaplan, (New York: Samuel Weiser, 1979).

[26] Such a leap is alluded to in the heroic tale of Rabbi Shimon Bar Yochai and his son who fled to a cave in the Judean desert to escape Roman persecution. For 12 years they ate only carobs from a nearby tree and drank water from a natural source in close proximity. During the hours of daylight, they stood neck-deep in sand-filled holes to preserve their clothes. Throughout this period of physical hardship and pain from blisters and heat, the mystical text of the *Zohar (The Book of Splendor)* was revealed to Rabbi Yochai to channel this source book of Jewish mystical teachings. By shifting his attention to this higher purpose, he was able to transcend to a higher state of consciousness beyond the reach of suffer-

ing and disease. So too, if we can focus on the higher purpose of our existence, we can leave our suffering behind and make the leap to a higher consciousness.

27 Colette explained: The horizontal line or axis represents the events of our everyday life. The vertical line or axis is the ladder of possibilities before us. When both lines meet, we have the opportunity to leave the limitations of the space/time dimension.

28 For an anatomic drawing to facilitate your visualization, see, for example, *The Anatomy Coloring Book* by Wynn Kapit and Lawrence M. Elson, (New York: Harper Collins College Publishers, 1993).

29 Recently, a friend of mine was found to have colon cancer. I went to visit her and gave the exercise "Taking Your Life in Your Hands," from Phase One. In her imagery, she looked at her new plant, and saw a beautiful flower grow up, up, up, until it reached Heaven, and there she heard the verse, "A righteous person will flourish like a date-palm" (Psalms 92:13). The date palm is revered for all it provides in food and shelter. Its trunk grows straight up with all its branches crowning its top. Her image evoked her vertical connection to the heavens and to the Sabbath experience. The weekly celebration of a Sabbath allows us to step out of our habitual connection to time and experience eternity, a taste of Eden. See my books *Achoti Kalla-My Sister My Bride* and *I Need a Soul Companion!*

30 Colette Aboulker-Muscat, *Alone with the One,* (New York: ACMI Press, 1995) 80.

31 Aboulker-Muscat, Alone *with the One,* 42.

32 *Tov L'Hodot* by Binyamin Tsadik who elevates hip-hop music to songs of praise for his Maker; his compositions may be heard at: www.soundclick.com/binyamintsadik.

33 Drawn from the sage Judah Halevy.

34 May this story help elevate the soul of Ariel ben Mordechai high up in Eden.

35 I am grateful to Raeph Sanderson for sharing this story with me.

[36] Colette Aboulker-Muscat, *Life is Not a Novel: A Child of the Century's Life Story,* Trans. Francoise Coriat, (MA: Black Jasmine, 2003).

[37] A city on the Mediterranean cost of Algeria.

[38] All translations are from the French by the author.

[39] Aliza Yehezkiel, *The Davidic Families and the Genealogy of Colette Aboulker-Muscat,* (Jerusalem: 2005). ISBN 965-90295-0-0. Available from the author at alizay@bezeqint.net.

[40] Gita Amipaz-Silber, *La Resistance Juive en Algerie 1940–1942,* (Jerusalem: Rubin Mass Ltd., 1986).

[41] Robert Desoille, *Le Rêve-Eveille en Psychothérapie: Essai sur la Fonction de Régulation de l'inconscient Collectif,*(Paris: Presses Universitaires de France, Paris, 1945).

[42] Mishnah: *Peah* 1; Talmud: *Shabbat* 127a.

[43] Epstein, *Healing Into Immortality,* 197.

[44] Some of my religious Jewish clients in Jerusalem corrected the image as follows: They saw themselves as part of the collective soul of Israel, knowing that fixing an error is easier when done together as a whole community than when tackled as a single individual. Following the imaginal repair, they attended group prayer meetings for women desiring to repair any spiritual damage caused by an abortion or other errors that weigh heavily on them. The prayer meetings are organized several times a year by an institute for Torah studies in Jerusalem. I have included the article *Repairing Inner Cancer* on my website www.healingwithinwithout.com/ with the intention of helping each woman perform this quality of repair within the privacy of her own home. The intention of the group is to repair any damage done to the love relationship with the One so each may declare, "I found the One my soul loves. I held Him and would not let Him go [determined that my deeds would never again cause me to lose hold of Him]" Paraphrasing the Song of Songs 3:4. Avraham Sutton, Trans. *The Breslov Siddur: Nusach Sefard.* Vol. II (Breslov Research Institute, Jerusalem/NY, 2014), forthcoming, on the sabbath experience.

[45] Epstein, *Healing Into Immortality,* 98–99.

46 When you enter an imaginal circle or look into an imaginal mirror you are entering another dimensional reality where your ability to communicate with the Divine realm is enhanced.

47 I am grateful to Carol Rose, MA, a student of Colette's, as well as a writer, educator, and spiritual counselor, for suggesting this technique to identify elusive figures in visual imagery.

48 Norman Cousins, *Head First: The Biology of Hope and the Healing Power of the Human Spirit*, (New York: E. P. Dutton, 1990) 217, quoting Dr. Bahnson of the *National Cancer Institute*. Cousins adds: "Since cancer patients tend to report lower levels of emotional distress than their observed behavior or measurements of unconscious affect would indicate, Dr. Bahnson said that it was essential in the study of cancer patients to measure unconscious psychological states using interviews or tests that allowed for more free association, such as story completion and picture interpretation."

Index

abortions, addressing, 41, 192–93

Aboulker-Muscat, Colette
    background, xi–xiv, 3, 6–8
    cleansing as the key to healing, 15, 37
    dream therapy, 215
    gangrened leg, healing of, 169–70
    harmony in relationships, restoring, 213–14
    healing of patients, 17–18, 165–67, 173–74, 176–77
    as heroine of Algerian resistance movement, 172
    on horizontal and vertical lines, 230n27
    illness, seeing the good in, 42
    imagery as Language of the Divine, 9
    images, use in healing process, 19
    last days and death of, 177, 178–81
    light, ascending to, 132
    living as vibrating, 113
    on the lower and Higher Self, 182
    message of detachment for sufferers, 133
    Mount Sinai, inner journey to, 170–71
    on physical action after cleansing guilt, 84
    poems of, 156–57
    psychology, studying and teaching, 175
    repair of relationships with the departed, 219
    reversing technique and success in healing, 13
    separation of intention from attention, healing through, 21
    Source of Life ascension as favorite healing technique, 41
    star connection experience, 167–68

tips and instructions on exercises, 16, 25, 78, 149, 152, 187–88, 194
anxiety, relieving, 72–83, 189, 196

Baruch, Henry, 173–74
Benyosef, Simcha H., xi, xiv, 131–32, 155–56, 180, 181, 237

cancer
    cancer diagnosis, first response, 3
    detachment from worry, 133, 152
    emotional stress or sudden shock as contributors, 9–10
    fear, letting go of, 4, 185
    feelings, failure to recognize or identify, 216
    imagery work and, 29
    new level of consciousness, helping to reach, 42
    new path, opening, xi
    reversing and turning away from cancer, 13, 14, 35, 43
    shift in awareness before cure, 11–12
    stress and, 5
    targeted healing visualizations
        brain cancer, 138–40
        breast cancer, 140
        colon cancer, 140–41
        leukemia, 141–42
        liver cancer, 142–43
        lung cancer, 143–44
        ovarian cancer, 144
        skin cancer, 144–45
    See also tumors
chemotherapy, 40, 41, 137, 146–47
Chopra, Deepak, 11–12

Desoille, Robert, 174
disease, detaching and separating from, 98–107, 108–112

Epstein, Gerald, 3, 18, 24
exercises
    ascent exercises, 219–20, 220–22, 222–25
    cleansing exercises, 37–39
    danger, exercises for threats of, 158–59
    diagnostic exercises, 203–06
    examples of healing through exercises, 207–13
    guilt, exercises to remove, 17, 50, 84–93, 189
    Higher Self, connecting with via healing exercises
        37, 136, 141, 183-84
    imagery exercises to eliminate fear, 64, 87, 135–36, 149, 151, 153–54
    monthly exercises, choosing, 40
    nighttime reversing exercises, 15–16, 134–35, 194–95, 195–200,
        200–01
    post-surgical exercises, 149–51
    reconnection exercises, 183–88
    tips for getting started, 42–43
    warm-up exercises, 30–32
    Way to Paradise exercise, 17, 219–20, 222–25
    See also phases

family in imagery work, 32, 46–48, 86, 88, 121, 159
fear
    before checkups, 133
    future fears, burden of, 15
    illness, fear magnifying under, 152
    imagery exercises, helping to deal with, 64, 87, 135–36, 149, 151,
        153–54
    letting go, fear prior to, 160
    of metastasis/recurrence, 4, 21, 134

guilt
    abortions, due to, 192
    bad food choices, causing, 200
    blame and, 124
    brain cleansing exercise, removing guilt through, 138
    camera exercise, alleviating, 50

cancer, guilt for having created, 10–11
cleansing guilt exercises, 84–93
departed loved ones, guilty feelings towards, 178, 219–20
as a habit, 15
pail and water exercise, relieving, 189
reversing of, 14
Way to Paradise exercise, helping to ease, 17

Higher Self
    conscious awareness of, 178
    defining, 23–24
    healing, Higher Self facilitating, 9, 182, 185
    healing exercises, connecting to Higher Self through, 37, 136, 141,
        183–84
    personal images stemming from, 203
    restoration of self-image and, 18
    reversing techniques, creating connection with, 13–14, 15

imagery
    conditioned emotional responses, separating from, 15
    customization of imagery program, 40–42
    detachment from suffering, 6
    fantasy, as differing from, 24
    function of, 8
    Higher Self, contacting through, 23
    as homeopathy of the mind, 18
    length of exercises and timing, 27–28
    posture and breathing, 25–27, 43
    proficiency in imagery, 14
    repetition of images, 13, 29
    shift in awareness, cultivated through, 12
    as a subjective experience, xiii
    as a tool of repair, 4
    See also exercises; phases

Kübler-Ross, Elizabeth, 10–11

letting go process, 159–61
lions in imagery work, 50–51, 68

metastasis, fear of, 4, 21

nausea, shedding, 148
nighttime reversing exercises, 15–16, 134–35, 194–95, 195–200, 200–01

pain, letting go of, 154–55
phases
    overview, 36
    one, re-rooting through tree imagery, 44–48
    two, messages from the body to the mind, 49–58
    three, gaining control over out-of-order body parts, 59–65
    four, reversing, use of to reconnect with Source of Life, 66–71
    five, elimination of anxiety, 72–83
    six, cleansing of guilt, 84–93
    seven, removal of resentment, 94–97
    eight, detachment from disease and knowing the Higher Self, 98–
        107
    nine, separation and distance from disease, 108–12
    ten, vibration bringing joy, 113–16
    eleven, identification and cleansing of harmful emotions, 117–125
    twelve, initiation of ascent towards growth, 126–132
prayer
    as an enduring function, 28
    Colette and, 156, 169, 180
    before exercises, 40, 42
    group prayer meetings in Jerusalem, 231n44
    repair, as a form of, 88
    of thanksgiving, 147, 150
    treatment, prior to, 202

radiation, 137, 146–48
relationships, repairing, 213–19

resentment, clearing, 94–97
reversing techniques
    defining, 13
    four types of reversing, 14–16
    Higher Self, calling upon to reverse illness, 182
    imagery use in reversing techniques, 19, 43
    nighttime reversing exercises, 15–16, 134–35, 194–95, 195–200,
        200–01
    pail and water applications, 17, 189–90, 201, 203, 208, 211
    reconnection with Source of Life through reversal, 66

side effects, removing, 149
surgery, recovering from, 41, 149–51

tree of life in visualization exercises, 90, 183–84
trees in imagery work, 44–46, 90, 119, 120, 122, 144–45, 167–68
tumors, 4, 40, 41, 43, 137, 138–140, 145, 149

visualization techniques. *See* exercises; imagery; phases

warm-up exercises, 30–32
Way to Paradise exercise, 17, 219–20, 222–25
worry, 47, 78, 133–36

About Simcha H. Benyosef

Simcha H. Benyosef abandoned a successful academic career to move to Israel in 1986. There, Benyosef was able to pursue a life long interest in the inner dimension of Torah, as taught first by Rabbi Aryeh Kaplan and then by the Chasidic Sage Rabbi Moshe Luria. In Jerusalem, Benyosef met Madame Colette Aboulker-Muscat, a therapist and master of visual imagery. Under Colette's tutelage, Benyosef discovered the means to use the healing powers of the mind and spirit to overcome disease. Benyosef focused on the application of Colette's mental imagery to heal from cancer, devising a unique 12-step program.

Other books by the author include:

The Beginning of Wisdom:
Unabridged Translation of the Gate of Love from Rabbi Elijah De Vidas' Reshit Chochmah.

Living Kabbalah:
A Guide to the Sabbath and the Festivals in the Teachings of Rabbi Rafael Moshe Luria.

The Light of Ephraim:
The Ascent from Temptation to Divine Consciousness

Empowered to Heal:
Therapeutic Visualizations Drawn for the Lunar Months.

Achoti Kalla-My Sister My Bride:
Learning to Enhance the Shabbat Experience

I Need a Soul Companion!
A Novel on the Shabbat Mystery

Simcha Benyosef can be reached at simchahbenyosef@yahoo.com.

Lightning Source UK Ltd.
Milton Keynes UK
UKHW041309110219
337100UK00001B/78/P